TIRRA LIRRA

RHYMES OLD AND NEW

Foreword by
MAY HILL ARBUTHNOT

With Illustrations by
MARGUERITE DAVIS

Boston · LITTLE, BROWN AND COMPANY · *Toronto*

TIRRA LIRRA

Rhymes Old and New

by

LAURA E. RICHARDS

Fifteenth Printing

Published simultaneously in Canada
by Little, Brown & Company (Canada) Limited

PRINTED IN THE UNITED STATES OF AMERICA

To

JOHN RICHARDS II,
my youngest grandchild,

AND

WILLIAM DAVIS TICKNOR III,
my eldest great-grandchild:

TWO VERY YOUNG GENTLEMEN

Tirra lirra, little John!
Tirra lirra, tiny Bill!
Take my hurdy-gurdy, boys;
Turn it with a will!
In the sun and in the rain,
Sing and play and sing again;
Be you clown or be you king,
Still your singing is the thing.
But be sure, my little boys,
That you make a joyful noise!

L. E. R.

To my Mother,

JULIA WARD HOWE

Sweet! when first my baby ear
Curled itself and learned to hear,
'T was your silver-singing voice
Made my baby heart rejoice.

Hushed upon your tender breast,
Soft you sang me to my rest;
Waking, when I sought my play,
Still your singing led the way.

Cradle songs, more soft and low
Than the bird croons on the bough;
Olden ballads, grave and gay,
Warrior's chant, and lover's lay.

So my baby hours went
In a cadence of content,
To the music and the rhyme
Keeping tune and keeping time.

So you taught me, too, ere long,
All our life should be a song, —
Should a faltering prelude be
To the heavenly harmony;

And with gracious words and high,
Bade me look beyond the sky,
To the Glory throned above,
To th' eternal Light and Love.

Many years have blossomed by:
Far and far from childhood I;
Yet its sunrays on me fall,
Here among my children all.

So among my babes I go,
Singing high and singing low;
Striving for the silver tone
Which my memory holds alone.

If I chant my little lays
Tunefully, be yours the praise;
If I fail, 't is I must rue
Not t' have closelier followed you.

DEDICATION OF
"In My Nursery", 1890

ACKNOWLEDGMENTS

My thanks are due to the following publishers and periodicals for permission to reprint copyrighted poems included in this book as follows:

To L. C. Page and Company, Boston, for "The Poor Unfortunate Hottentot", "Dog-gerel", "Prince Tatters", and "The Gargoyle and the Griffin" from "The Hurdy Gurdy", copyright, 1902, by L. C. Page and Company; also "Some Families of My Acquaintance", "Jeremi' and Josephine", "The Uncle of Cato Theophilus Jones", "After a Visit to the Natural History Museum", "The Gingham Umbrella", "In Foreign Parts", "A Spanish Ballad", and "A Brief Ballad of Araby" from "The Piccolo", copyright, 1906, by L. C. Page and Company.

To *St. Nicholas* for "The Mameluke and the Hospodar", "The Polar Bear's Party", "Roderigo and Ferdinando", "Why I No Longer Travel", "The Ambitious Haddock", "Various Persons", "Bingo the Dingo and the Fatal Flamingo", and "Good Advice."

To *Child Life* for "The High Barbaree", "Eletelephony", "The Man and the People", "The Maid of Timbuctoo", "The Buffalo", "The Unfortunate Grocer", "The Greedy Giant", "Talents Differ", "Sir Ringleby Rose", "Kindness to Animals", "Story-Tell", and "Spots and Stripes."

To *Saturday Review of Literature* for "The Brigand and the Actor" and "The Crocodile."

Sixty-three of the poems in this book are from my book, "In My Nursery", published by Little, Brown, and Company.

LAURA E. RICHARDS

"A JOYFUL NOISE"

When Laura E. Richards was a cheerful eighty-two-years-old and a new edition of her verses for children was about to be published, she wrote a dedication to her youngest grandchild and her eldest great-grandchild, "Two Very Young Gentlemen." It is not only free of the advice the aged usually bestow upon their descendants but has the light touch so characteristic of the author. She always referred to the songs that bubbled up within her as "my hurdy-gurdy." So, after willing the hurdy-gurdy to her boys, she concludes:

> *Be you clown or be you king,*
> *Still your singing is the thing.*
> *But be sure, my little boys,*
> *That you make a JOYFUL noise!*

For most of her ninety-three years the hurdy-gurdy turned out songs, stories, jingles and dances of such infectious gaiety that they live on because children and grownups won't let them go.

Laura E. Richards came by her singing naturally. She tells us that her mother, the beautiful Julia Ward Howe, sang to her children in five languages. When those children were grown she wrote "The Battle Hymn of the Republic," which set the whole nation to singing from that day to this.

The children of Julia Ward Howe grew up singing. But after she was a mother, Laura discovered that tucked away in her mind somewhere, she had a special music box all her own. If it never sounded the organ notes of a "Battle Hymn," it certainly entranced the children. She would use the broad back of her current baby as a writing board, and all seven babies in turn gurgled and jounced to their mother's jingles.

TUNES AND RHYTHMS

Children have been clapping or chanting these jingles ever since, for they are as full of catchy tunes as a songbook and their rhythms are as compelling as a jig. Small children go choo-choo-chooing round the room to the "Jiggle joggle jee!" of "The Baby Goes to Boston." Each verse of this Tunerville Trolley ends with still another train rhythm:

> *Loky moky poky stoky*
> *Smoky choky chee!*

Sleep-resistant bairns grow drowsy and drift off with "Johnny's By-Low Song":

> *Where all the flowers go niddlety nod,*
> *Nod, nod, niddlety nod!*

And in contrast to these soporific verses, no child can resist the lively "Pip! pop! flippety flop!" chorus of "The Song of the Corn Popper" or the exuberant marching refrain of "The Umbrella Brigade":

> *But let it rain*
> *Tree-toads and frogs,*
> *Muskets and pitchforks,*

xii

Kittens and dogs!
Dash away! plash away!
Who is afraid?
Here we go,
The Umbrella Brigade!

These and others are action songs with melodies as evident as if they had been set to notes. Children chant them, sing them or play them with delight.

STORY SURPRISES

Children also chuckle over the story poems. These frequently begin mildly but conclude with a bang. There is for instance, the story of "The Seven Little Tigers and the Aged Cook." The tigers had every intention of eating the aged cook but instead . . . Well, *six* of the tigers were pleased and so was the cook.

Less shocking is the tale of "Little John Bottlejohn," who seems to have been a cheerful soul with a house on the top of a hill. Nothing extraordinary about that, if he had just stayed there. But alas! John went down the hill to interview a mermaid, with sad results.

A more hilarious shocker is "Mrs. Snipkin and Mrs. Wobblechin," two quarrelsome old characters, one of whom comes to a bad end. The children roll the names under their tongues and like the catastrophic conclusion.

"My Uncle Jehoshaphat," who had a swimming race with his pig, "Jippy and Jimmy," and other little verse stories are well liked, but the prize of them all is "The Monkeys and the Crocodile." Its popularity is probably due to the fact that most children have tasted the

xiii

sad results of seeing how far they can go before they "catch it." So the fate of the fifth monkey not only tickles their funny bones but they remark sternly, "It served him right, too."

It is a temptation to go on listing poem after poem that has given special pleasure to this child or that classroom. But isn't it significant that every time this book we know as *Tirra Lirra* goes out of print it is reissued by popular demand? That is the case with this edition. Schools today, and parents who remember these jingles from their own childhood, will not let the songs be silenced. And schools and homes must keep them alive, for here are nonsense verses deftly composed by an author with an ear for the melody of words and a keen sense of the dramatic and the ludicrous. The gentle satire of "Prince Tatters," the absurd confusion of "Eletelephony," the joke about "The Egg" or the little girl who turned the tables on the smug robin in "Talents Differ," these are a sure cure for the doldrums, laughter conveniently packaged between the covers of a book. That is important, for solemnities are ever present in every age. Children and grownups need to laugh together, and no hurdy-gurdy ever turned out gayer tunes or made a more joyful noise than Laura E. Richards's *Tirra Lirra*.

MAY HILL ARBUTHNOT

Cleveland, Ohio

CONTENTS

TIRRA LIRRA

RHYMES OLD AND NEW

A LEGEND OF LAKE OKEEFINOKEE

THERE once was a frog,
And he lived in a bog,
On the banks of Lake Okeefinokee.
And the words of the song
That he sang all day long
Were, "Croakety croakety croaky."

Said the frog, "I have found
That my life's daily round
In this place is exceedingly poky.
So no longer I 'll stop,
But I swiftly will hop
Away from Lake Okeefinokee."

Now a bad mocking-bird
By mischance overheard
The words of the frog as he spokee.
And he said, "All my life

I

Frog and I 've been at strife,
As we lived by Lake Okeefinokee.

"Now I see at a glance
Here 's a capital chance
For to play him a practical jokee.
So I 'll venture to say
That he shall not to-day
Leave the banks of Lake Okeefinokee."

So this bad mocking-bird,
Without saying a word,
He flew to a tree which was oaky,
And loudly he sang,
Till the whole forest rang,
"Oh! Croakety croakety croaky!"

As he warbled this song,
Master Frog came along,
A-filling his pipe for to smokee;
And he said, "'T is some frog
Has escaped from the bog
Of Okeefinokee-finokee.

"I am filled with amaze
To hear one of my race
A-warbling on top of an oaky;
But if frogs can climb trees,
I may still find some ease
On the banks of Lake Okeefinokee."

So he climbed up the tree;
But alas! down fell he!
And his lovely green neck it was brokee;
And the sad truth to say,
Never more did he stray
From the banks of Lake Okeefinokee.

And the bad mocking-bird
Said, "How very absurd
And delightful a practical jokee!"
But I 'm happy to say
He was drowned the next day
In the waters of Okeefinokee.

THE MAMELUKE AND THE HOSPODAR

A MESOPOTAMIAN Mameluke
　Was pricking it over the plain;
He met a Wallachian Hospodar,
　Riding about in the rain.

"How now, my wild Wallachian fellar?
　Why do you go without an umbrella?"
"For that, alas! I am not to blame;
　I'm trying to find a rhyme for my name!"

Spoken

Mameluke: "If your name were Hosporus,
　　　　　That would rhyme with Bosporus."
Hospodar: "Yes, but it is n't, and so it does n't.
　　　　　You make my brain reel, and you
　　　　　muzz n't."

4

Both :   "Great is truth and shall prevail,
               Therefore must we weep and wail."

"And you, O Mameluke Mesopotamian,"
  Queried the Hospodar,
"What are *you* doing, my glad and gamy un,
  Galloping off so far?

"Tell me, I pray, ere you forget,
  I 'm really getting rather wet."
"A quest like yours, sir, I pursue,
  Seeking a rhyme for my name, too."

Spoken

Hospodar :   "If your first name were Sammy Luke
           That would rhyme with Mameluke."
Mameluke : "Yes, but it is n't, and so it does n't.
           You make my eyes squint, and you
           muzz n't."
Both :   "Great is truth and shall prevail,
           Therefore must we weep and wail."

Cantando, gallopando

"Ride we off through the rainy weather,
Mameluke, Hospodar, both together;
  Search and sorrow for both the same,
  Neither can find a rhyme for his name!"

5

THE POOR UNFORTUNATE HOTTENTOT

A POOR unfortunate Hottentot
He was not content with his lottentot;
  Quoth he, "For my dinner,
  As I am a sinner,
There 's nothing to put in the pottentot!"

This poor unfortunate Hottentot
Said, "Yield to starvation I 'll nottentot;
  I 'll see if I can't elope
  With a young antelope, —
One who 'll enjoy being shottentot."

This poor unfortunate Hottentot
His bow and his arrows he gottentot;
  And being stout-hearted,
  At once he departed,
And struck through the Bush at a trottentot.

This poor unfortunate Hottentot,
Was not many miles from his cottentot,
   When he chanced to set eyes on
   A snake that was pison,
A-tying itself in a knottentot.

This poor unfortunate Hottentot
Remarked, "This for me is no spottentot!
   I 'd better be going;
   There 's really no knowing;
I might on his view be a blottentot."

This poor unfortunate Hottentot,
Was turning to fly to his grottentot,
   When a lioness met him,
   And suddenly ate him,
As penny's engulfed by the slottentot.

Moral

This poor unfortunate Hottentot,
Had better have borne with his lottentot.
   A simple banana
   Had staved off Nirvana;
But what had become of my plottentot?

8

LITTLE JOHN BOTTLEJOHN

LITTLE John Bottlejohn lived on the hill,
  And a blithe little man was he.
And he won the heart of a pretty mermaid
  Who lived in the deep blue sea.
And every evening she used to sit
  And sing on the rocks by the sea,
"Oh! little John Bottlejohn, pretty John Bottlejohn,
  Won't you come out to me?"

Little John Bottlejohn heard her song,
  And he opened his little door.
And he hopped and he skipped, and he skipped and he
    hopped,
  Until he came down to the shore.
And there on the rocks sat the little mermaid,
  And still she was singing so free,
"Oh! little John Bottlejohn, pretty John Bottlejohn,
  Won't you come out to me?"

Little John Bottlejohn made a bow,
  And the mermaid, she made one too;
And she said, "Oh! I never saw any one half
  So perfectly sweet as you!
In my lovely home 'neath the ocean foam,
  How happy we both might be!
Oh! little John Bottlejohn, pretty John Bottlejohn,
  Won't you come down with me?"

Little John Bottlejohn said, "Oh yes!
  I 'll willingly go with you.

And I never shall quail at the sight of your tail,
    For perhaps I may grow one too."
So he took her hand, and he left the land,
    And plunged in the foaming main.
And little John Bottlejohn, pretty John Bottlejohn,
    Never was seen again.

THE HIGH BARBAREE *

As I was sailing down the coast
  Of High Barbaree,
I chanced to see a Muffin Bird
  A-sitting in a tree.

Oh, mournfully he sang,
  And sorrowful he sat,
Because he was a-frightened of
  The Crum-pet Cat !

The Crumpet Cat is little known ;
  He sits him under trees,
And watches for the Muffin Bird
  His palate for to please.

And then he opens wide his mouth,
  The cruel Crumpet Cat,
And the Muffin Bird falls into it,
  Just — like — *that !*

I left the ship, I gained the shore,
  And to the tree I hied,
Just as the Cat was opening
  His jaws wide, wide !

I waved my arms and shouted loud,
  "Shoo ! *shoo!* SHOO!"
And off the Cat went flumpering,
  And off the birdie flew.

Moral

When you sail the Barbaree,
  Mind what you 're about !
Always carry with you
  A good loud shout !

When you see a Crumpet Cat,
  Let your shout be heard ;
For you may save the life of
  A pretty Muffin Bird !

    * "Sailing down along the coast
      Of the High Barbaree."
                — *Old Song*

12

DOG–GEREL

I sat beside a lady fair,
   A lady grave and sweet;
Withal so wise, that well I might
   Have sat me at her feet.
She stooped to pat the puppy dog
   That gambolled at her knee;
And when she spoke, 't was in a tongue
   Was wholly strange to me.

"A wizzy wizzy woggums, then!
   A ditty dotty doggums, then!
And diddy wanty dumpy up?
   A pitty witty pessums pup!"

I spoke to her of foreign climes,
   Of politics and popes;
Of Bishop Bylow's pious rhymes,
   And General Jingo's hopes.
She answered well and wittily,
   Then turned her eyes aside,

And tenderly she whispered to
   The creature by her side.

"A pupsy wupsy keeter, then!
   Was never nossin sweeter, then!
A teenty tawnty tiny tot,
   A lovely dovely darling dot!"

I rose at length and strolled away,
   Not wishing to intrude;
Yet thought perhaps she 'd bid me stay,
   And rather hoped she would.
But no! she never raised her head.
   I turned the corner near,
And as I went, her silver tones
   Still floated to my ear.

"A toodle toodle toodle, then!
   A wisky wasky woodle, then!
A 'toopid manny gone, my joy,
   My diddy doddy dorglums boy!"

THE Rummy-jums, the Rummy-jums,
  Are very funny people;
(Very, very, very, very,
  Very funny people!)
They run as hard as they can go,
  And clamber up the steeple;
(Clamber-climber, climber-clamber,
  Clamber up the steeple!)
And when they get up to the top,
They say, "Good gracious, we must stop!"
And turn about with grief and pain,
And clamber-climber down again.

The Viddipocks, the Viddipocks,
  Have very pretty bonnets:
(Very, very, very, very,
  Very pretty bonnets!)
And when they wear them upside down,
  They write most lovely sonnets;
(Lovely-dovely, dovely-lovely,
  Lovely-dovely sonnets!)
And sitting on the new-mown hay,
They wirble-warble all the day;
"For oh," they say, "at such a time,
Our very ribbons flow in rhyme!"

The Wiggle-wags, the Wiggle-wags,
  They never know their mind, sir;

(Never, never, never, never,
  Never know their mind, sir!)
Sometimes they hook their frocks before,
  And sometimes up behind, sir;
(Hook them, crook them, crook them, hook them,
  Hook them up behind, sir!)
And first they turn them inside out,
Then outside-inside with a shout;
"For oh," they say, "there's no one knows
Which way the most our beauty shows!"

THE POLAR BEAR'S PARTY

OR

THE MANNERLESS MUSK OX

A HOSPITABLE Polar Bear
  Resolved to give a party;
His nature was gregarious,
  His sentiments were hearty.

He asked the Walruses and Seals
  That lived upon the floe;
And in a burst of friendliness
  The Musky Ox also.

"The Musky Ox he lives on land,
  But still, he likes it cold;
His fur is thick, he 's never sick;
  I think I 'll make so bold!"

"O Musky Ox, O Husky Ox,
  Your neighbor,* Polar Bear,
Invites you to his party;
  He hopes you 'll come; so there!"

A lovely feast of blubber strips
  He set before each guest,
A puffin pie, a stuffin' pie,
  And boobies of the best.

* Not a very near neighbor, but I 'd just as lief be a hundred
miles from the Pole as close to it, would n't you? Or *would n't*
you?

17

They drank — I don't know what they drank,
  But they were blithe and gay,
And still the more the viands shrank,
  The more they had to say.

All, all except the Musky Ox!
  He sat beside the board;
He did not eat, he did not drink,
  He did not speak a word.

"Speak up! speak up! thou Musky Ox,
  Why sit so dumb and still?
The rest are merry as you please,
  And eat and drink their fill."

The Musk Ox raised his musky eyes,
  And shook his musky head;
"I don't like blubber, you ursine lubber,"
  He very rudely said.

"Your puffin pie, your stuffin' pie,
    They fill me with disgust,
Bring me, old hoss, some Iceland moss !
    You will, you shall, you must !"

The Bear looked at the Walruses,
    And they looked back at him,
They rose beside the festal board,
    And oh, their looks were grim.

"Go seek your Iceland moss yourself,
    You rude unmannered beast ;
It will be long before you 're asked
    To share a Polar feast !"

They seized upon that Musky Ox,
    And drove him to the shore ;
They bundled him, they trundled him,
    With loud and angry roar.

Now see him wallop o'er the snow,
    Hungry and tired and cross,
For not within a hundred miles
    Grew any Iceland moss.

While Bear and Walruses and Seals
    Cry, "Wherefore all this fuss ?
E'en let him go, old Double-Toe !
    There 's all the more for us !" *

* This was not polite, either.   He had been very rude to them,
but two wrongs don't make a right !

MORAL

Eat what is set before you,
And don't be rude or cross,
And when you dine with Polar Bears,
Don't ask for Iceland Moss!

A SONG FOR HAL

ONCE I saw a little boat, and a pretty, pretty boat,
When daybreak the hills was adorning,
And into it I jumped, and away I did float,
So very, very early in the morning.

> *Chorus.*　And every little wave had its nightcap on,
> Its nightcap, white cap, nightcap on.
> And every little wave had its nightcap on,
> So very, very early in the morning.

All the fishes were asleep in their caves cool and deep,
When the ripple round my keel flashed a warning.
Said the minnow to the skate, "We must certainly be
　　late,
Though I thought 't was very early in the morning."

Chorus. For every little wave has its nightcap on,
Its nightcap, white cap, nightcap on.
For every little wave has its nightcap on,
So very, very early in the morning.

The lobster darkly green soon appeared upon the scene,
And pearly drops his claws were adorning.
Quoth he, "May I be boiled, if I 'll have my slumber
    spoiled,
So very, very early in the morning!"

Chorus. For every little wave has its nightcap on,
Its nightcap, white cap, nightcap on,
For every little wave has its nightcap on,
So very, very early in the morning.

Said the sturgeon to the eel, "Just imagine how I feel,
Thus roused without a syllable of warning.
People ought to let us know when a-sailing they would
    go,
So very, very early in the morning."

Chorus. When every little wave has its nightcap on,
Its nightcap, white cap, nightcap on.
When every little wave has its nightcap on,
So very, very early in the morning.

Just then up jumped the sun, and the fishes every one
For their laziness at once fell a-mourning.
But I stayed to hear no more, for my boat had reached
    the shore,
So very, very early in the morning.

22

Chorus.   And every little wave took its nightcap off,
Its nightcap, white cap, nightcap off.
And every little wave took its nightcap off,
And curtsied to the sun in the morning.

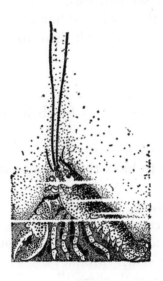

THE ORANG-OUTANG

Orang-outang-tang,
Oring-outing-ting,
He set himself up to be king-outing-ting.
  He called up the Gibbons,
  And decked them with ribbons,
And vowed he would teach them to sing-outing-ting.

Orang-outang-tang,
Orong-outong-tong,
Said, "Some one must play for their song-outong-tong."
  He called the Baboons,
  And he gave them bassoons,
And told them to blow them along-outong-tong.

Orang-outang-tang,
Orung-outung-tung,
He called up the Monkeys so young-outung-tung.
  But when he said, "Monkeys,
  I 'll dress you as flunkeys!"
Away to the forest they sprung-outung-tung.

Oring-outing-ting,
Orang-outang-tang,
He bounced off his throne with a bang-outang-tang.
  "I don't care for ruling,
  It 's pesky and puling,
The kingdoms of earth may go hang-outang-tang."

THE BRIGAND AND THE ACTOR

Have you heard of Belonzo the Brigand,
   Who lived on the top of the Alps?
How graceful he was in the jig, and
   How deft in the shaving of scalps?

Have you heard how he captured an actor
   (Though from the profession he shrank!)
And took him to ride on a tractor,
   And taught him to coast in a tank?

Have you heard how the captive dissembled
   His feelings, and said it was fun,
Though 't was plain to be seen that he trembled
   When sent down a peak on the run?

Have you heard how they hunted the Gnoodle
   (So rare in the Alps, as you know!)
And how they sang "Toodle cum toodle",
   While chasing it over the snow?

Have you heard how an avalanche caught them
   And tumbled them down from on high;
How vainly their followers sought them?
   You have n't? No more, dear, have I!

25

MRS. SNIPKIN AND MRS. WOBBLECHIN

SKINNY Mrs. Snipkin,
  With her little pipkin,
Sat by the fireside a-warming of her toes.
  Fat Mrs. Wobblechin,
  With her little doublechin,
Sat by the window a-cooling of her nose.

  Says this one to that one,
  "Oh ! you silly fat one,
Will you shut the window down ? You 're freezing me
  to death !"
  Says that one to t' other one,
  "Good gracious, how you bother one !
There is n't air enough for me to draw my precious
  breath !"

  Skinny Mrs. Snipkin,
  Took her little pipkin,

Threw it straight across the room as hard as she could
    throw;
        Hit Mrs. Wobblechin
        On her little doublechin,
And out of the window a-tumble she did go.

POT AND KETTLE

*[To be read to little boys and girls who quarrel
with each other]*

"Oнo! Oho!" said the pot to the kettle,
"You 're dirty and ugly and black!
Sure no one would think you were made of metal,
Except when you 're given a crack."

"Not so! not so!" kettle said to the pot.
"'T is your own dirty image you see.
For I am so clear, without blemish or blot,
That your blackness is mirrored in me."

THE QUEEN OF THE ORKNEY ISLANDS

Oh! the Queen of the Orkney Islands,
She's travelling over the sea :
She's bringing a beautiful cuttlefish,
To play with my baby and me.

Oh! his head is three miles long, my dear,
His tail is three miles short.
And when he goes out he wriggles his snout,
In a way that no cuttlefish ought.

Oh! the Queen of the Orkney Islands,
She rides on a sea-green whale.
He takes her a mile, with an elegant smile,
At every flip of his tail.

He can snuffle and snore like a Highlandman,
And swear like a Portugee;
He can amble and prance like a peer of France,
And lie like a heathen Chinee.

Oh! the Queen of the Orkney Islands,
She dresses in wonderful taste;
The sea-serpent coils, all painted in oils,
Around her bee-you-tiful waist.

Oh! her gown is made of the green sea-kale;
And though she knows nothing of feet,
She can manage her train, with an air of disdain,
In a way that is perfectly sweet.

Oh! the Queen of the Orkney Islands,
She's travelling over the main.
So we'll hire a hack, and we'll take her straight back
To her beautiful Islands again.

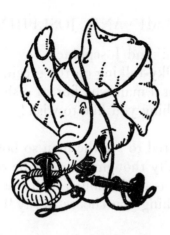

ELETELEPHONY

ONCE there was an elephant,
Who tried to use the telephant —
No! no! I mean an elephone
Who tried to use the telephone —
(Dear me! I am not certain quite
That even now I 've got it right.)

Howe'er it was, he got his trunk
Entangled in the telephunk;
The more he tried to get it free,
The louder buzzed the telephee —
(I fear I 'd better drop the song
Of elephop and telephong!)

JEREMI' AND JOSEPHINE

As Jeremi' and Josephine
Were walky-talking on the green,
They met a man who bore a dish
Of (anything you like to wish!)

They stared to see the man so bold;
They really thought he must be cold,
For he was clad, though chill the day,
In (anything you choose to say!)

The man returned their stare again;
But now the story gives me pain,
For he remarked in scornful tone,
(I 'll let you manage this alone!)

And there is even worse to come;
The man (I 've been informed by some)
Inflicted on the blameless two
(I leave the punishment to you!)

This simple tale is thus, you see,
Divided fair 'twixt you and me,
And nothing more I 've heard or seen
Of Jeremi' or Josephine.

ALICE'S SUPPER

Far down in the meadow the
    wheat grows green,
And the reapers are whetting their
    sickles so keen;
And this is the song that I hear
    them sing,
While cheery and loud their voices
    ring:
"'T is the finest wheat that ever
    did grow!
And it is for Alice's supper, ho! ho!"

Far down in the valley the old mill stands,
And the miller is rubbing his dusty white
    hands;
And these are the words of the miller's lay,
As he watches the millstones a-grinding
    away:
"'T is the finest flour that money can buy,
And it is for Alice's sup-
    per, hi! hi!"

Downstairs in the kitchen
    the fire doth glow,
    And Maggie is kneading
the soft white dough,
And this is the song that she's sing-
    ing to-day,
While merry and busy she's working
    away:

33

"'T is the finest dough by near or by far,
And it is for Alice's supper, ha! ha!"

And now to the nursery comes Nannie at last,
And what in her hand is she bringing so fast?
'T is a plate full of something all yellow and white,
And she sings as she comes with her smile so bright:
"'T is the best bread-and-butter I ever did see!
And it is for Alice's supper, he! he!"

THE MAN AND THE PEOPLE

In Nijni — Nijni-Novgorod,
There lived a Man whose ways were odd;
He took his Aunt Katinka's bonnet,
And fastened frubjub feathers on it,
Then capering both low and high,
Exclaimed, "O People, see me fly!"

The People saw, and said, "Go to!
That's not at all the way to do.
Our indignation you must brave,
If better you do not behave.
You look like neither bird nor bat;
We really wonder what you're at."

"If you don't like the way I fly,"
Replied the Man, "I now will try
To please you in another manner.
Of my accomplishments, the banner
One I will show to please your whim;
Come! you shall see the way I swim!"

He took the fins of foodle fish,
(They'd served him for his noonday dish),
And strapped them to each arm and leg.
"Now to the riverside, I beg!
See! in the flood I bravely plunge!
Look! through the waves I lightly lunge.
I do assure you, perfect bliss!
Now saw you ever aught like this?"

The People all with one accord
Exclaimed, "We never did! my word!
You 're not a frog, you 're not a fish;
We haste to say, our only wish
Concerning you is that you 'd go
And not come back again, you know."

The Man, depressed, departed thence;
The People heaved a sigh immense.
"Good riddance to him! for in sooth,
If we must speak the simple truth,
We don't, in Nijni-Novgorod,
Care much for folk whose ways are odd!"

SOME FISHY NONSENSE

TIMOTHY TIGGS and Tomothy Toggs,
They both went a-fishing for pollothywogs;
    They both went a-fishing
    Because they were wishing
To see how the creatures would turn into frogs.

Timothy Tiggs and Tomothy Toggs,
They both got stuck in the bogothybogs;
    They caught a small minnow,
    And said 't was a sin oh!
That things with no legs should pretend to be frogs.

JUMBO JEE

THERE were some kings, in number three,
Who built the tower of Jumbo Jee.
They built it up to a monstrous height,
At eleven o'clock on a Thursday night.

They built it up for forty miles,
With mutual bows and pleasing smiles;
And then they sat on the edge to rest,
And partook of lunch with a cheerful zest.

And first they ate of the porkly pie,
And wondered why they had built so high;
And next they drank of the ginger wine,
Which gave their noses a regal shine.

They drank to the health of Jumbo Jee,
Until they could neither hear nor see.
They drank to the health of Jumbo Land,
Until they could neither walk nor stand.

They drank to the health of Jumbo Tower
Until they really could drink no more;
And then they sank in a blissful swoon,
And flung their crowns at the rising moon.

AN INDIAN BALLAD

WHOPSY WHITTLESEY WHANKO WHEE,
Howly old, growly old Indian he,
Lived on the hills of the Mungo-Paws,
With all his pappooses and all his squaws.
There was Wah-wah-bocky, the Blue-nosed Goose,
And Ching-gach-gocky, the Capering Moose :
There was Peeksy Wiggin, and Squaw-pan too,
But the fairest of all was Michiky Moo.
Michiky Moo, the Savory Tart,
Pride of Whittlesey Whanko's heart ;
Michiky Moo, the Cherokee Pie,
Apple of Whittlesey Whanko's eye.
Whittlesey Whanko loved her so
That the other squaws did with envy glow ;
And each said to the other, "Now, what shall we do
To spoil the beauty of Michiky Moo ?"
"We 'll lure her away to the mountain top,
And there her head we will neatly chop."
"We 'll wile her away to the forest's heart,
And shoot her down with a poisoned dart."
"We 'll lead her away to the river-side,

And there she shall be the Manito's bride."
"Oh! one of these things we will surely do,
And we'll spoil the beauty of Michiky Moo."
"Michiky Moo, thou Cherokee Pie,
Away with me to the mountain high!"
"Nay, my sister, I will not roam;
I'm safer and happier here at home."
"Michiky Moo, thou Savory Tart,
Away with me to the forest's heart!"
"Nay! my sister, I will not go;
I fear the dart of some hidden foe."
"Michiky Moo, old Whittlesey's pride,
Away with me to the river-side!"
"Nay! my sister, for fear I fall!
And wouldst thou come if thou heardst me call?"
"Now choose thee, choose thee thy way of death!
For soon thou shalt draw thy latest breath!
We all have sworn that this day we'll see
The last, proud Michiky Moo, of thee!"
Whittlesey Whanko, hidden near,
Each and all of these words did hear.
He summoned his braves, all painted for war,
And gave them in charge each guilty squaw:
"Take Wah-wah-bocky, the Blue-nosed Goose;
Take Ching-gach-gocky, the Capering Moose;
Take Peeksy Wiggin, and Squaw-pan too,
And leave me alone with my Michiky Moo.
This one away to the mountain top,
And there her head ye shall neatly chop;
This one away to the forest's heart,

And shoot her down with a poisoned dart;
This one away to the river-side,
And there she shall be the Manito's bride;
Away with them all, the woodlands through!
For I 'll have no squaw save Michiky Moo."
Away went the braves, without question or pause,
And they soon put an end to the guilty squaws.
They pleasantly smiled when the deed was done,
Saying, "Ping-ko-chanky! oh! is n't it fun!"
And then they all danced the Buffalo dance,
And capered about with ambiguous prance,
While they drank to the health of the lovers so true,
Bold Whittlesey Whanko and Michiky Moo.

THE EGG

OH! how shall I get it, how shall I get it, —
A nice little new-laid egg?
My grandmamma told me to run to the barn-yard,
And see if just one I could beg.

"Moolly-cow, Moolly-cow, down in the meadow,
Have you any eggs, I pray?"
The Moolly-cow stares as if I were crazy,
And solemnly stalks away.

"Oh! Doggie, Doggie, perhaps you may have it,
That nice little egg for me."
But Doggie just wags his tail and capers,
And never an egg has he.

"Now, Dobbin, Dobbin, I'm sure you must have one,
Hid down in your manger there."

But Dobbin lays back his ears and whinnies,
With "Come and look, if you dare!"

"Piggywig, Piggywig, grunting and squealing,
Are you crying 'Fresh eggs for sale'?"
No! Piggy, you're very cold and unfeeling,
With that impudent quirk in your tail.

"You wise old Gobbler, you look so knowing,
I'm sure you can find me an egg.
You stupid old thing! just to say 'Gobble-gobble!'
And balance yourself on one leg."

Oh! how shall I get it, how shall I get it, —
That little white egg so small?
I've asked every animal here in the barn-yard,
And they won't give me any at all.

But after I'd hunted until I was tired,
I found — not one egg, but ten!
And you *never* could guess where they all were hidden, —
Right under our old speckled hen!

WILL-O'-THE-WISP

"Will-o'-the-wisp! Will-o'-the-wisp!
   Show me your lantern true!
Over the meadow and over the hill,
   Gladly I 'll follow you.
Never I 'll murmur nor ask to rest,
   And ever I 'll be your friend,
If you 'll only give me the pot of gold
   That lies at your journey's end."

Will-o'-the-wisp, Will-o'-the-wisp,
   Lighted his lantern true;
Over the meadow and over the hill,
   Away and away he flew.
And away and away went the poor little boy,
   Trudging along so bold,
And thinking of naught but the journey's end,
   And the wonderful pot of gold.

Will-o'-the-wisp, Will-o'-the-wisp,
   Flew down to a lonely swamp;
He put out his lantern and vanished away
   In the evening chill and damp.
And the poor little boy went shivering home,
   Wet and tired and cold;
He had come, alas! to his journey's end,
   But where was the pot of gold?

PRINCE TATTERS

LITTLE Prince Tatters has lost his cap!
  Over the hedge he threw it;
Into the river it fell *kerslap!*
  Stupid old thing, to do it!
Now Mother may sigh and Nurse may fume
For the gay little cap with its eagle plume.
"One cannot be thinking all day of such matters!
Trifles are trifles!" says little Prince Tatters.

Little Prince Tatters has lost
    his coat!
  Playing, he did not need it;
"Left it *right there*, by the
    nanny-goat,
  And nobody never seed
    it!"

Now Mother and Nurse may search till night
For the new little coat with its buttons bright;
But "Coat sleeves or shirt sleeves, how little it matters!
Trifles are trifles!" says little Prince Tatters.

Little Prince Tatters has LOST HIS BALL!
  Rolled away down the street!
Somebody 'll *have to find it*, that's all,
  Before he can sleep or eat.
Now raise the neighborhood quickly, do!
And send for the crier and constable, too!
"Trifles are trifles, but serious matters,
They must be *seen to*," says little Prince Tatters.

THE MAID OF TIMBUCTOO

A LOVELY maid of Timbuctoo
  She loved a Bedouin so true,
She stole her uncle's choicest scarab
To buy tobacco for her Arab.
    Sing ba ha ha ! and boo hoo hoo !
  The lovely maid of Timbuctoo !

Her uncle was a savage chief ;
  He swore he 'd hang the rascal thief
Who stole withouten dread or fear
The beetle that he held so dear.
    Sing ba ha ha ! and boo hoo hoo !
  The lovely maid of Timbuctoo !

The maid crept out, her love to see ;
  The uncle followed after she,
And saw her give, and heard her tell
About the deed she 'd planned so well.
    Sing ba ha ha ! and boo hoo hoo !
  The lovely maid of Timbuctoo !

He took his billowy burnoos,
  And twisted it into a noose,
And to a palm tree's shady cover
He hanged the maiden and her lover !
    Sing ba ha ha ! and boo hoo hoo !
  The lovely maid of Timbuctoo !

MORAL

Maids! if your uncle is an Arab,
  Don't steal his highly valued scarab;
Or you may meet in palmy shade
The fate that met this hapless maid.
  Sing ba ha ha! and boo hoo hoo!
  The lovely maid of Timbuctoo!

THE CROCODILE

WHY does the crocodile weep, Mamma?
  Why does the crocodile weep?
He has a sorrow, dear my child;
It makes him sad, it makes him wild;
  He cannot be a sheep!

He cannot wag a woolly tail,
  He cannot say, "Ba! ba!"
He cannot jump, nor flimp nor flump,
  Nor gallop off afar.

Be sorry for the crocodile,
  But don't go very near;
Howe'er he bawl, whate'er befall,
  Don't try to dry his tear!

THE LITTLE COSSACK

THE tale of the little Cossack,
Who lived by the river Don :
He sat on a sea-green hassock,
And his grandfather's name was John.
His grandfather's name was John, my dears,
And he lived upon bottled stout ;
And when he was found to be not at home,
He was frequently found to be out.

The tale of the little Cossack, —
He sat by the riverside,
And wept when he heard the people say
That his hair was probably dyed.
That his hair was probably dyed, my dears,
And his teeth were undoubtedly sham ;
"If this be true," quoth the little Cossàck,
"What a poor little thing I am !"

The tale of the little Cossack, —
He sat by the river's brim,
And he looked at the little fishes,
And the fishes looked back at him.
The fishes looked back at him, my dears,
And winked at him, which was wuss ;
"If this be true, my friend," they said,
"You 'd better come down to us."

The tale of the little Cossack, —
He said, "You are doubtless right,

Though drowning is not a becoming death,
For it makes one look like a fright.
If my lovely teeth be crockery,
And my hair of Tyrian dye,
Then life is a bitter mockery,
And no more of it will I !"

The tale of the little Cossack, —
He drank of the stout so brown;
Then put his toes in the water,
And the fishes dragged him down.
And the people threw in his hassock
And likewise his grandfather John;
And there was an end of the family,
On the banks of the river Don.

TO THE LITTLE GIRL WHO WRIGGLES

DON'T wriggle about any more, my dear!
I 'm sure all your joints must be sore, my dear!
It 's wriggle and jiggle, it 's twist and it 's wiggle,
Like an eel on a shingly shore, my dear,
Like an eel on a shingly shore.

Oh! how do you think you would feel, my dear,
If you should turn into an eel, my dear?
With never an arm to protect you from harm,
And no sign of a toe or a heel, my dear,
No sign of a toe or a heel?

And what do you think you would do, my dear,
Far down in the water so blue, my dear,
Where the prawns and the shrimps, with their curls
      and their crimps,
Would turn up their noses at you, my dear,
Would turn up their noses at you?

The crab he would give you a nip, my dear,
And the lobster would lend you a clip, my dear.
And perhaps if a shark should come by in the dark,
Down his throat you might happen to slip, my dear,
Down his throat you might happen to slip.

Then try to sit still on your chair, my dear!
To your parents 't is no more than fair, my dear.
For we really don't feel like inviting an eel
Our board and our lodging to share, my dear,
Our board and our lodging to share.

51

THE MOUSE

I 'M only a poor little mouse, Ma'am.
I live in the wall of your house, Ma'am.
With a fragment of cheese,
And a *very few* peas,
I was having a little carouse, Ma'am.

No mischief at all I intend, Ma'am.
I hope you will act as my friend, Ma'am.
If my life you should take,
Many hearts it would break,
And the mischief would be without end, Ma'am.

My wife lives in there, in the crack, Ma'am,
She's waiting for me to come back, Ma'am.
She hoped I might find
A bit of a rind,
For the children their dinner do lack, Ma'am.

'T is hard living there in the wall, Ma'am,
For plaster and mortar *will* pall, Ma'am,

52

On the minds of the young,
And when specially hung —
Ry, upon their poor father they 'll fall, Ma'am.

I never was given to strife, Ma'am, —
(Don't look at that terrible knife, Ma'am!)
The noise overhead
That disturbs you in bed,
'T is the rats, I will venture my life, Ma'am.

In your eyes I see mercy, I 'm sure, Ma'am.
Oh, there 's no need to open the door, Ma'am.
I 'll slip through the crack,
And I 'll never come back,
Oh! I 'll *never* come back any more, Ma'am!

RODERIGO AND FERDINANDO

R<small>ODERIGO</small> was a peasant,
  And he lived in Basquerie;
Ferdinando was a pheasant,
  Tenderly beloved of he.

Roderigo's lot was humble,
  But the pheasant, gold-besprent,
Made the envious neighbors grumble,
  Which increased his heart's content.

Roderigo by the hour
  Gloated o'er his cherished bird,
While his friends would stand and glower,
  Muttering, "You *are* absurd!"

Ponderoso was a Baron
  Living in a castle grim,

54

And he envied Roderigo,
    'Cause the pheasant b'longed to him.

"Sell me now your pleasant pheasant!"
    Said the brawny Baron bold,
"I have need of him at present,
    And you 've doubtless need of gold."

"Go away!" said Roderigo,
    "To your castle home return!
Or depart to far Oswego;
    It is none of my concern.

"Ferdinando is my darling,
    But I tell you, Baron grim,
I will change him to a starling,
    Ere you lay a hand on him!"

(Roderigo, simple peasant,
    Dealt in magic, so they say,
And he *could* make things unpleasant,
    In a necromantic way.)

Ponderoso disbelieved him,
    Vowed the pheasant he would steal,
But his destiny deceived him,
    By the turn of Fortune's wheel.

Ent'ring Roderigo's cabin,
    Searching for the precious fowl,

Suddenly he felt a stab in
  Vital parts that made him howl.

'T was the pheasant! for the present
  To a sharp-billed starling changed,
Jabbing him with jabs unpleasant
  As around the cot he ranged.

Shrieking fled poor Ponderoso,
  Squawking followed him the bird,
All the way unto his castle
  Were his yells of anguish heard.

And the starling, ("*Such* a darling!"
  As good Roderigo said :)
Changing back in manner pleasant,
Shone once more the golden pheasant,
Saying, "Let 's enjoy the present!"
  Perched on Roderigo's head.

THE FORTY LITTLE DUCKLINGS

[A story with a certain amount of truth in it]

THE forty little ducklings who lived up at the farm,
They said unto each other, "Oh! the day is very
    warm!"
They said unto each other, "Oh! the river's very cool!
The duck who did not seek it now would surely be a
    fool."

The forty little ducklings, they started down the road;
And waddle, waddle, waddle, was the gait at which
    they goed.
The same it is not grammar, — you may change it if
    you choose, —
But one cannot stop for trifles when inspired by the
    Muse.

They waddled and they waddled and they waddled on
    and on,
Till one remarked, "Oh! deary me, where *is* the river
    gone?
We asked the Ancient Gander, and he said 't was very
    near.
He must have been deceiving us, or else himself, I fear."

They waddled and they waddled, till no further they
    could go:
Then down upon a mossy bank they sat them in a
    row.

They took their little handkerchiefs and wept a little
　　weep,
And then they put away their heads, and then they
　　went to sleep.

There came along a farmer, with a basket on his arm,
And all those little duckylings he took back to the farm.
He put them in their little beds, and wished them
　　sweet repose,
And fastened mustard plasters on their little webby
　　toes.

Next day these little ducklings, they were very, very ill.
Their mother sent for Doctor Quack, who gave them
　　each a pill ;
But soon as they recovered, the first thing that they did,
Was to peck the Ancient Gander, till he ran away and
　　hid.

THE MERMAIDENS

THE little white mermaidens live in the sea,
In a palace of silver and gold ;
And their neat little tails are all covered with scales,
Most beautiful for to behold.

On wild white horses they ride, they ride,
And in chairs of pink coral they sit ;
They swim all the night, with a smile of delight,
And never feel tired a bit.

THE PHRISKY PHROG

Now list, oh! list to the piteous tale
Of the Phrisky Phrog and the Sylvan Snayle;
Of their lives and their loves, their joys and their woes,
And all about them that any one knows.

The Phrog lived down in a grewsome bog,
The Snayle in a hole in the end of a log;
And they loved each other so fond and true,
They did n't know what in the world to do.

For the Snayle declared 't was too cold and damp
For a lady to live in a grewsome swamp;
While her lover replied, that a hole in a log
Was no possible place for a Phrisky Phrog.

"Come down! come down, my beautiful Snayle!
With your helegant horns and your tremulous tail;
Come down to my bower in the blossomy bog,
And be happy with me," said the Phrisky Phrog.

"Come up, come up, to my home so sweet,
Where there 's plenty to drink, and the same to eat;
Come up where the cabbages bloom in the vale,
And be happy with me," said the Sylvan Snayle.

But he would n't come, and she would n't go,
And so they could never be married, you know;
Though they loved each other so fond and true,
They did n't know what in the world to do.

60

WHY I NO LONGER TRAVEL

In Kalamazoo, in Kalamazoo,
  The very first man I met
Was riding a race on a brindled gnu ;
He said, "And how do you doodle doo,
  My lithesome, blithesome pet ?"

In Sagadahoc, in Sagadahoc,
  The people I chanced to see
Had turned their heads hindside before ;
"We find it attracts attention more !"
  They kindly explained to me.

In Valladolid, in Valladolid,
  As soon as I came in sight,
The people all ran away and hid ;
'T was just the same whatever I did,
  I could not think it was right.

And that is the reason, in travelling season,
  Why I no longer roam ;
Except round here, folks *are* so queer,
  I 'm really better at home.

A VALENTINE

Oh, little loveliest lady mine!
What shall I send for your valentine?
Summer and flowers are far away,
Gloomy old Winter is king to-day,
Buds will not blow, and sun will not shine;
What shall I do for a valentine?

Prithee, Saint Valentine, tell me here,
Why do you come at this time o' year?
Plenty of days when lilies are white,
Plenty of days when sunbeams are bright;
But now, when everything's dark and drear,
Why do you come, Saint Valentine dear?

I 've searched the gardens all through and through,
For a bud to tell of my love so true;
But buds are asleep, and blossoms are dead,
And the snow beats down on my poor little head;
So, little loveliest lady mine,
Here is my heart for your valentine.

THE SHARK

Oh! blithe and merrily sang the shark,
  As he sat on the house-top high:
A-cleaning his boots, and smoking cheroots,
  With a single glass in his eye.

With Martin and Day he polished away,
  And a smile on his face did glow,
As merry and bold the chorus he trolled
  Of "Gobble-em-upsky ho!"

He sang so loud, he astonished the crowd
  Which gathered from far and near.

For they said, "Such a sound, in the country round,
    We never, no, never did hear."

He sang of the ships that he'd eaten like chips
    In the palmy days of his youth.
And he added, "If you don't believe it is true,
    Pray examine my wisdom tooth!"

He sang of the whales who'd have given their tails
    For a glance of his raven eye.
And the swordfish, too, who their weapons all drew,
    And swor'd for his sake they'd die.

And he sang about wrecks and hurricane decks
    And the mariner's perils and pains,
Till every man's blood up on end it stood,
    And their hair ran cold in their veins.

But blithe as a lark the merry old shark,
    He sat on the sloping roof.
Though he said, "It is queer that no one draws near
    To examine my wisdom toof!"

And he carolled away, by night and by day,
    Until he made every one ill.
And I'll wager a crown that unless he's come down,
    He is probably carolling still.

THE POSTMAN

HEY! the little postman,
　　And his little dog.
Here he comes a-hopping
　　Like a little frog;
Bringing me a letter,
　　Bringing me a note,
In the little pocket
　　Of his little coat.

Hey! the little postman,
　　And his little bag,
Here he comes a-trotting
　　Like a little nag;
Bringing me a paper,
　　Bringing me a bill,
From the little grocer
　　On the little hill.

Hey! the little postman,
　　And his little hat,
Here he comes a-creeping
　　Like a little cat.
What is that he's saying?
　　"Naught for you to-day!"
Horrid little postman!
　　I wish you'd go away!

NONSENSE VERSES

I

NICHOLAS NED,
He lost his head,
And put a turnip on instead ;
But then, ah me !
He could not see,
So he thought it was night, and he went to bed.

II

Ponsonby Perks,
He fought with Turks,
Performing many wonderful works ;
He killed over forty,
High-minded and haughty,
And cut off their heads with smiles and smirks.

III

Winifred White,
She married a fright,
She called him her darling, her duck, and delight ;
The back of his head
Was so lovely, she said,
It dazzled her soul and enraptured her sight.

IV

Harriet Hutch,
Her conduct was such,
Her uncle remarked it would conquer the Dutch:
She boiled her new bonnet,
And breakfasted on it,
And rode to the moon on her grandmother's crutch.

THE UMBRELLA BRIGADE

"PITTER patter!" falls the rain
On the school-room window-pane.
Such a plashing! such a dashing!
Will it e'er be dry again?
Down the gutter rolls a flood,
And the crossing's deep in mud;
And the puddles! oh, the puddles
Are a sight to stir one's blood!

Chorus.   But let it rain
          Tree-toads and frogs,
          Muskets and pitchforks,
          Kittens and dogs!
          Dash away! plash away!
          Who is afraid?
          Here we go,
          The Umbrella Brigade!

Pull the boots up to the knee!
Tie the hoods on merrily!
Such a hustling! such a jostling!
Out of breath with fun are we.
Clatter, clatter, down the street,
Greeting every one we meet,
With our laughing and our chaffing,
Which the laughing drops repeat.

Chorus.   So let it rain
          Tree-toads and frogs,

Muskets and pitchforks,
Kittens and dogs !
Dash away ! plash away !
Who is afraid ?
Here we go,
The Umbrella Brigade !

MY CLOCK

My little clock, my little clock,
He lives upon the shelf;
He stands on four round golden feet,
And so supports himself.

His face is very white and clean,
His hands are very black;
He has no soap to wash them with,
And suffers from the lack.

He holds them up, his grimy hands,
And points at me all day;
"Make haste, make haste, the moments waste!"
He always seems to say.

"Tick tock! tick tock! I am a clock;
I 'm always up to time.
Ding dong! ding dong! the whole day long
My silver warnings chime.

"Tick tock! tick tock! 't is nine o'clock,
And time to go to school;
Don't loiter 'mid the buttercups,
Or by the wayside pool.

"Ding dong! tick tock! 't is one o'clock.
The dinner 's getting cold;
You 'd better hurry down, you child,
Or your mamma will scold.

"Tick tock! tick tock! 't is six o'clock.
You 've had the afternoon
To play and romp, so now come in;
Your tea 'll be ready soon.

"Tick tock! tick tock! 't is nine o'clock.
To bed, to bed, my dear!
Sleep sound, until I waken you,
When day is shining clear."

So through the night and through the day,
My busy little clock,
He talks and talks and talks away,
With ceaseless "tick" and "tock."

But warning others on his shelf,
All earnest as he stands,
He never thinks to warn himself;
He 'll *never* wash his hands.

THE MONKEYS AND THE CROCODILE

FIVE little monkeys
Swinging from a tree;
Teasing Uncle Crocodile,
Merry as can be.
Swinging high, swinging low,
Swinging left and right:
"Dear Uncle Crocodile,
Come and take a bite!"

Five little monkeys
Swinging in the air;

Heads up, tails up,
  Little do they care.
Swinging up, swinging down,
  Swinging far and near:
"Poor Uncle Crocodile,
  Are n't you hungry, dear?"

  Four little monkeys
  Sitting in the tree;
Heads down, tails down,
  Dreary as can be.
Weeping loud, weeping low,
  Crying to each other:
"Wicked Uncle Crocodile,
  To gobble up our brother!"

THE AMBITIOUS HADDOCK

THERE once was a haddock
Who lived in a paddock,
   (A singular statement, if true!)
Who said to his wife,
"The desire of my life
   Is to turn to a quaint Kangaroo.

"Evolution, they say,
Is the word of the day,
   And men were once fishes, I'm told;
Why may not a fish
Have his heart's dearest wish,
   If he be but sufficiently bold?"

So this valorous haddock
(Who fed upon shaddock!
   There's *no* other food that will rhyme!)
He strove without fail
To grow legs and tail,
   For a time and a time and a time.

He wriggled apace
All over the place,
   He flopped and he flapped and he strove;
But he stayed just the same,
And the people who came
   Said, "Who *is* this cantankerous cove?"

His wifey flopped by
With a sob and a sigh,

And said, "Won't you drop it, my dear?
There 's no sign of a change,
And your conduct 's *so* strange,
    You will end in the lockup, I fear!"

He developed a Voice,
But he could not rejoice,
    His outcries grew louder and louder;
Till a housewife came by
With a gleam in her eye,
    And said, "*I* will change you — to Chowder!"

ALIBAZAN

ALL on the road to Alibazan,
A May Day in the morning,
'T was there I met a bonny young man,
A May Day in the morning;
A bonny young man all dressed in blue,
Hat and feather and stocking and shoe,
Ruff and doublet and mantle, too,
A May Day in the morning.

He made me a bow, and he made me three,
A May Day in the morning;
He said, in truth, I was fair to see,
A May Day in the morning.
"And say, will you be my sweetheart now?
I 'll marry you truly with ring and vow;
I 've ten fat sheep and a black-nosed cow,
A May Day in the morning.

"What shall we buy in Alibazan,
A May Day in the morning?
A pair of shoes and a feathered fan,
A May Day in the morning.
A velvet gown all set with pearls,
A silver hat for your golden curls,
A pot of pinks for my pink of girls,
A May Day in the morning."

All in the streets of Alibazan,
A May Day in the morning,

The merry maidens tripped and ran,
A May Day in the morning.
And this was fine, and that was free,
But he turned from them all to look on me;
And "Oh! but there 's none so fair to see,
A May Day in the morning."

All in the church of Alibazan,
A May Day in the morning,
'T was there I wed my bonny young man,
A May Day in the morning.
And oh! 't is I am his sweetheart now!
And oh! 't is we are happy, I trow,
With our ten fat sheep and our black-nosed cow,
A May Day in the morning.

THE SEVEN LITTLE TIGERS AND THE
AGED COOK

SEVEN little tigers they sat them in a row,
Their seven little dinners for to eat;
And each of the troop had a little plate of soup,
The effect of which was singularly neat.

They were feeling rather cross, for they had n't any
    sauce
To eat with their pudding or their pie;
So they rumpled up their hair, in a spasm of despair,
And vowed that the aged cook should die.

Then they called the aged cook, and a frying-pan they
    took,
To fry him very nicely for their supper;
He was ninety-six years old, on authority I 'm told,
And his name was Peter Sparrow-piper Tupper.

"Mr. Sparrow-piper Tup, we intend on you to sup!"
Said the eldest little tiger very sweetly;
But this naughty aged cook, just remarking, "Only
    look!"
Chopped the little tiger's head off very neatly.

Then he said unto the rest, "It has always been con-
    fessed
That a tiger 's better eating than a man;
So I 'll fry him for you now, and you all will find, I
    trow,
That to eat him will be much the better plan."

So they tried it in a trice, and found that it was nice,
And with rapture they embracèd one another;
And they said, "By hook or crook, we must keep this
    aged cook;
So we 'll ask him to become our elder brother."
                       [Which they accordingly did.]

EMILY JANE

Oh ! Christmas time is coming again,
And what shall I buy for Emily Jane ?
O Emily Jane, my love so true,
Now what upon earth shall I buy for you ?
My Emily Jane, my doll so dear,
I 've loved you now for many a year,
And still while there 's anything left of you,
My Emily Jane, I 'll love you true !

My Emily Jane has lost her head,
And has a potato tied on instead ;
A hole for an eye, and a lump for a nose,
It really looks better than you would suppose.
My Emily Jane has lost her arms,
The half of one leg 's the extent of her charms ;
But still, while there 's anything left of you,
My Emily Jane, I 'll love you true !

And now, shall I bring you a fine new head,
Or shall I bring you a leg instead?
Or will you have arms, to hug me tight,
When naughty 'Lizabeth calls you a fright?
Or I 'll buy you a dress of satin so fine,
'Mong all the dolls to shimmer and shine;
For oh! while there 's anything left of you,
My Emily Jane, I 'll love you true!

Mamma says, "Keep all your pennies, Sue,
And I 'll buy you a doll all whole and new;"
But better I love my dear old doll,
With her one half-leg and potato poll.
"The potato may rot, and the leg may fall?"
Well, then I shall treasure the sawdust, that 's all!
For while there is *anything* left of you,
My Emily Jane, I 'll love you true!

THE BUFFALO

THE Buffalo, the Buffalo,
He had a horrid snuffle, oh!
And not a single Indian chief
Would lend the beast a handkerchief,
Which shows how very, very far
From courtesy those people are.

SONG OF THE MOTHER WHOSE CHILDREN ARE FOND OF DRAWING

Oh, could I find the forest
 Where the pencil-trees grow!
Oh, might I see their stately stems
 All standing in a row!
I'd hie me to their grateful shade,
 In deep, in deepest bliss;
For then I need not hourly hear
 A chorus such as this:

Chorus. Oh, lend me a pencil, *please*, Mamma!
 Oh, draw me some houses and trees, Mamma!
 Oh, make me a floppy
 Great poppy to copy,
 And a horsey that prances and gees, Mamma!

The branches of the pencil-tree
 Are pointed every one;
Ay! each one has a glancing point
 That glitters in the sun.
The leaves are leaves of paper white,
 All fluttering in the breeze;
Ah! could I pluck one rustling bough,
 I'd silence cries like these:

Chorus. Oh, lend me a pencil, *do*, Mamma!
 I've got mine all stuck in the glue, Mamma!
 Oh, make me a pretty
 Big barn and a city,
 And a cow and a steam engine too, Mamma!

The fruit upon the pencil-tree
    Hangs ripening in the sun,
In clusters bright of pocket-knives, —
    Three blades to every one.
Ah! might I pluck one shining fruit,
    And plant it by my door,
The pleading cries, the longing sighs,
    Would trouble me no more.
Chorus.   Oh, sharpen a pencil for *me*, Mamma!
    'Cause Johnny and Baby have three, Mamma!
    And this is n't fine!
    And Hal sat down on mine!
    So do it bee-yu-ti-ful-*lee*, Mamma!

THE UNFORTUNATE GROCER

THERE was a good grocer
Who never said, "No sir!"
  When dainties his customers sought.
Whatever their asking,
His brain he 'd be tasking,
  To buy anything could be bought.

Elephant's ear and tapir's tongue,
Pelican's pouch ("Be sure it 's young!")
Saddle of yak ("How long has it hung?")
  Ostrich's eggs ("New-laid!")
Buffalo milk ("Fermented!") to quaff,
Laughing jackass ("We want the laugh!")
And "Can't you get me a sucking giraffe?
  You 've always been amply paid!"

The unfortunate grocer
(Who never said, "No sir!")
  On hearing this, took to his bed.
"'T is hopeless to please them,
I never can ease them,
  I 'd better be dying!" he said.

PEEPSY

[After the manner of Jane Taylor]

Our Julia has a little bird,
    And Peepsy is his name;
And now I 'll sing a little song
    To celebrate the same.

He 's yellow all from head to foot,
    And he is very sweet,
And very little trouble, for
    He never wants to eat.

He never asks for water clear,
    He never chirps for seed,
For cracker, or for cuttlefish,
    For sugar or chickweed.

"Oh! what a perfect pet!" you cry,
    But there 's one little thing,
One drawback to the bonny bird, —
    Our Peepsy cannot sing.

He chirps no song at dawn or eve,
    He makes no merry din;
But this one cannot wonder at,
    For Peepsy 's made of tin.

87

VARIOUS PERSONS

An elderly lady named Mackintosh,
She went out to ride in a hackintosh;
    But the roads were so rough
    That she said in a huff,
"You may take me right speedily backintosh!"

A pallid professor named Pendleton
Exclaimed, "I have never a friendleton!
    They don't like my looks,
    And they won't read my books,
And I think it is time for my endleton."

A niggardly native of Buffalo,
Was strongly addicted to snuffalo;
    He roared at his wife,
    Till she feared for her life,
Because the cold mutton was toughalo.

PHIL'S SECRET

I KNOW a little girl,
But I won't tell who!
Her hair is of the gold,
And her eyes are of the blue.
Her smile is of the sweet,
And her heart is of the true.
Such a pretty little girl! —
But I won't tell who.

I see her every day,
But I won't tell where!
It may be in the lane,
By the thorn-tree there.
It may be in the garden,

By the rose-beds fair.
Such a pretty little girl! —
But I won't tell where.

I 'll marry her some day,
But I won't tell when!
The very smallest boys
Make the very biggest men.
When I 'm as tall as father,
You may ask about it then.
Such a pretty little girl! —
But I won't tell when.

THE SONG OF THE CORN-POPPER

Pip! pop! flippety flop!
Here am I, all ready to pop.
Girls and boys, the fire burns clear;
Gather about the chimney here.
Big ones, little ones, all in a row.
Hop away! pop away! here we go!

Pip! pop! flippety flop!
Into the bowl the kernels drop.
Sharp and hard and yellow and small;
Must say they don't look good at all.
But wait till they burst into warm white snow!
Hop away! pop away! here we go!

Pip! pop! flippety flop!
Don't fill me too full; shut down the top!
Rake out the coals in an even bed,
Topaz yellow and ruby red;
Shade your eyes from the fiery glow.
Hop away! pop away! here we go!

Pip! pop! flippety flop!
Shake me steadily; do not stop!
Backward and forward, not up and down;
Don't let me drop, or you'll burn it brown.
Never too high and never too low.
Hop away! pop away! here we go!

Pip! pop! flippety flop!
Now they are singing, and soon they 'll hop.
Hi! the kernels begin to swell;
Ho! at last they are dancing well.
Puffs and fluffs of feathery snow,
Hop away! pop away! here we go!

Pip! pop! flippety flop!
All full, little ones?   Time to stop!
Pour out the snowy, feathery mass;
Here is a treat for lad and lass.
Open your mouths now, all in a row;
Munch away! crunch away! here we go!

THE GREEDY GIANT

THERE once was a giant
So far from compliant,
  He would n't eat toast with his tea.
"A substance so horrid
Brings pains in my forehead,
  And aches in my toe-toes," said he, said he,
  "And aches in my toe-toes," said he.

They brought him a tartlet
To cheer up his heartlet,
  They brought him both jelly and jam;
But still while he gobbled,
He sighed and he sobbled,
  "You *don't* know how hungry I am, I am,
  You don't *know* how hungry I am!"

They brought him a cruller
To make him feel fuller,
  They brought him some pancakes beside,
They brought him a muffin,
On which he was stuffin',
  When all of a sudden he died, he died,
  When all of a sudden he died.

THE THREE FISHERS

John, Frederick, and Henry,
  Had once a holiday;
And they would go a-fishing,
  So merry and so gay.
They went to fish for salmon,
  These little children three;
As in this pretty picture
  You all may plainly see.

It was not in the ocean,
  Nor from the river shore,
But in the monstrous water butt
  Outside the kitchen door.
And John he had a fishhook,
  And Fred a crooked pin,

And Henry took his sister's net,
  And thought it was no sin.

They climbed up on the ladder,
  Till they the top did win;
And then they perched upon the edge,
  And then they did begin.
But how their fishing prospered,
  Or if they did it well,
Or if they caught the salmon,
  I cannot, cannot tell.

Because I was not there, you know,
  But I can only say
That I, too, went a-fishing,
  That pleasant summer day.
It was not for a salmon,
  Or shark with monstrous fin,
But it was for three little boys,
  All dripping to the skin.

SANDY GODOLPHIN

SANDY GODOLPHIN sat up on the hill,
And up on the hill sat he ;
And the only remark he was known to make,
Was "Fiddledy diddledy dee!"

He made it first in the high Hebrew,
And then in the Dutch so low,
In Turkish and Russian and Persian and Prussian,
And rather more tongues than I know.

He made this remark until it was dark,
And he could no longer see ;
Then he lighted his lamp, because it was damp,
And gave him the neuralgee.

Sandy Godolphin came down from the hill,
And moaned in a dark despair :
"I 've finished," said he, "with my fiddledy dee,
For nobody seems to care."

LADY'S SLIPPER (*Yellow*)

My lady she rose from her bower, her bower,
  All under the linden tree.
'T was midnight past, and the fairies' hour,
  And up and away must she.

She 's pulled on her slippers of golden yellow,
  Her mantle of gossamer green ;
And she 's away to the elfin court,
  To wait on the elfin queen.

Oh hone ! my lady's slipper,
  Oh hey ! my lady's shoe.
She 's lost its fellow, so golden yellow,
  A-tripping it over the dew.

And now she flitted, and now she stepped,
  Through dells of the woodland deep,
Where owls were flying awake, awake,
  And birds were sitting asleep.

And now she flitted, and now she trod,
  Where the mist hung shadowy-white ;
And the river lay gleaming, sleeping, dreaming,
  Under the sweet moonlight.

Oh hone ! my lady's slipper,
  Oh hey ! my lady's shoe.
She 's lost its fellow, so golden yellow,
  A-tripping it over the dew.

And now she passed through the wild marsh land,
  Where the marsh-elves lay asleep;
And a heron blue was their watchman true,
  Good watch and ward for to keep.

But Jack-in-the-Pulpit was wake, awake,
  And saw my lady gay;
And he reached his hand as she fluttered past,
  And caught her slipper away.

Oh hone! my lady's slipper,
  Oh hey! my lady's shoe.
She's lost its fellow, so golden yellow,
  A-tripping it over the dew.

Oh! long that lady she searched and prayed,
  And long she wept and besought;
But all would not do, and with one wee shoe
  She must dance at the elfin court.

But she *might* have found her slipper, her slipper,
  It shone so golden-gay;
For I am no elf, yet I found it myself,
  And I brought it home to-day.

Oh hone! my lady's slipper,
  Oh hey! my lady's shoe.
She's lost its fellow, so golden yellow,
  A-tripping it over the dew.

SING SONG

Sing, sing, what shall I sing?
  Sing of the lolloping lizard!
Too largely he dined,
And thereafter he pined,
  With a piteous pain in his gizzard.

Sing, sing, what shall I sing?
  Sing of the passionate poodle!
He screamed and he cried,
And he very near died,
  'Cause he could not pronounce "Cock-a-doodle."

Sing, sing, what shall I sing?
  Sing of the penitent panther!
He lived for three weeks
Upon lemons and leeks,
  Because he was rude to his gran'ther.

99

A PARTY

On Willy's birthday, as you see,
These little boys have come to tea.
But, oh! how very sad to tell!
They have not been behaving well.
For ere they took a single bite,
They all began to scold and fight.

The little boy whose name was Ned,
He wanted jelly on his bread ;
The little boy whose name was Sam,
He vowed he would have damson jam ;
The little boy whose name was Phil
Said, "I'll have honey! *Yes* — I — WILL!!"

BUT —

The little boy whose name was Paul,
While they were quarrelling, ate it all.

MY UNCLE JEHOSHAPHAT

My Uncle Jehoshaphat had a pig, —
  A pig of high degree;
And he always wore a brown scratch wig,
  Most beautiful for to see.

My Uncle Jehoshaphat loved this pig,
  And the piggywig he loved him;
And they both jumped into the lake one day,
  To see which best could swim.

My Uncle Jehoshaphat he swam up,
  And the piggywig he swam down;
And so they both did win the prize,
  Which the same was a velvet gown.

My Uncle Jehoshaphat wore one half,
  And the piggywig wore the other;
And they both rode to town on the brindled calf,
  To carry it home to its mother.

HE AND HIS FAMILY

His father was a whale,
With a feather in his tail,
Who lived in the Greenland sea;
And his mother was a shark,
Who kept very dark
In the Gulf of Caribbee.
His uncles were a skate,
And a little whitebait,
And a flounder, and a chub beside;
And a lovely pickerèl,
Both a beauty and a belle,
Had promised for to be his bride.
You may think these things are strange,
And they *are* a little change
From the ordinary run, 't is true;
But the queerest thing (to me)
Of all appeared to be,
That *he* was a kangaroo!

"TALENTS DIFFER"

"What are you doing there, Robin a Bobbin,
  Under my window, out in the blue?"
"Building my nest, O Little One, Pretty One,
  Doing the thing that you cannot do!"

"What are you doing now, Robin a Bobbin,
  Under my window, out in the blue?"
"Brooding my eggs, O Little One, Pretty One,
  Doing the thing that you cannot do!"

"What are you doing there, Robin a Bobbin,
  Under my window, out in the blue?"
"Feeding my nestlings, Little One, Pretty One,
  Doing the thing that you cannot do.

"And what are *you* doing, pray, Little One, Pretty One,
  What are you doing, tell me now true?"
"Sewing my patchwork, Robin a Bobbin,
  Doing the thing that *you* cannot do!"

103

TROPICAL CITIES

In the town of Chichen-Itza,
No one ever has a fit, sir;
And the reason, I declare,
Is that there is no one there.
You can't cure a fit, or save it,
If there's nobody to have it.

In the town of Bogotá,
(So I'm told) the people are
Striped and spotted, pink and blue,
(But I hardly think — do you?)
Anyhow it's rather far;
Let's not go to Bogotá!

In the mighty town of Rio,
There are wondrous things to see, oh!
Blue-eyed Binks a yard across,
Poskos playing pitch-and-toss,
Grinning Gabbies, drinking tea,
Dumpkins dancing merrily;
Bibulums and Bonkums, too,
That's the place for me and you!

LITTLE BLACK MONKEY

Little black Monkey sat up in a tree,
Little black Monkey he grinned at me;
He put out his paw for a cocoanut,
And he dropped it down on my occiput.

The occiput is a part, you know,
Of the head which does on my shoulders grow;
And it's very unpleasant to have it hit,
Especially when there's no hair on it.

I took up my gun, and I said, "Now, why,
Little black Monkey, should you not die?
I'll hit you soon in a vital part!
It may be your head, or it may be your heart."

I steadied my gun, and I aimed it true;
The trigger it snapped and the bullet it flew,
But just where it went to I cannot tell,
For I never *could* find where that bullet fell.

Little black Monkey still sat in the tree,
And placidly, wickedly grinned at me.
I took up my gun and I walked away,
And postponed his death till another day.

JIPPY AND JIMMY

JIPPY and Jimmy were two little dogs.
They went to sail on some floating logs;
The logs rolled over, the dogs rolled in,
And they got very wet, for their clothes were thin.

Jippy and Jimmy crept out again.
They said, "The river is full of rain!"
They said, "The water is far from dry!
Ki-hi! ki-hi! ki-*hi*-yi! ki-hi!"

Jippy and Jimmy went shivering home.
They said, "On the river no more we 'll roam;
And we won't go to sail until we learn how,
Bow-wow! bow-wow! bow-*wow*-wow! bow-wow!"

SIR RINGLEBY ROSE

Sir Ringleby Rose,
Sir Ringleby Rose,
He was not content with the shape of his nose.
He went to a witch,
Who lived in a ditch,
And asked could she alter it, did she suppose?

The witch said, "Oh!"
And then she said, "No!
To the Wizard of Wogg I advise you to go.
A specialist he,
Of the highest degree;
The noses he growses are wondrous to see."

Sir Ringleby Rose,
Sir Ringleby Rose,
He tottered away on his tribulous toes;
He found the old Wizard
Consulting his lizard
About the best poison to give to his foes.

The Wizard was frightfully busy that day,
He glanced at the knight in a casual way;
"What shape? What shape?
My elderly ape?
What shape, what shape?
Prithee speedily say!

"Will you have it Roman,
  O Man?

Will you have it Greek?
Shall it be a pugly wugly,
Or an eagle's beak?
Or will you have the transformation
    (Specialty of mine)
Known to each admiring nation
    As the Great Combine?"

Sir Ringleby Rose,
Sir Ringleby Rose,
Was flustered like mustard,
As you may suppose.
"A pugly is ugly,
A beak 's not my line.
Mayhap, my good chap,
I will try the Combine."

The Wizard of Wogg,
The Wizard of Wogg,
Did various things
With his Glimmering Glog.*
With cantrip commotion
He made up a potion,
And stirred it about
With the tail of a frog.

"Now wink and drink,
Sir Ringleby Rose!
Now wink and drink

* A magical instrument, little in use to-day.

109

Success to the Nose!
Then look in the glass,
And for what comes to pass
Ten guineas — I thank you —
Is all that you owes."

Sir Ringleby Rose,
Sir Ringleby Rose,
He wank and he drank,
With a hearty, "Here goes!"
But when in the glass
He saw *what* came to pass,
He fell down in a fit,
And he NEVER UPROSE!

MORAL

Be content with your nose.

MASTER JACK'S SONG

[Written after spending the Christmas Holidays at Grandmamma's]

You may talk about your groves,
Where you wander with your loves;
You may talk about your moonlit waves that fall and
    flow.
Something fairer far than these
I can show you, if you please.
'T is the charming little cupboard where the jam-pots
    grow.

Chorus.   Where the jam-pots grow!
            Where the jam-pots grow!
            Where the jelly jolly, jelly jolly jam-pots
                grow.
            The fairest spot to me,
            On the land or on the sea,
            Is the charming little cupboard where the
                jam-pots grow.

There the golden peaches shine
In their syrup clear and fine,
And the raspberries are blushing with a dusky
    glow;
And the cherry and the plum
Seem to beckon you to come
To the charming little cupboard where the jam-pots
    grow.

Chorus.   Where the jam-pots grow!
Where the jam-pots grow!
Where the jelly jolly, jelly jolly jam-pots
grow.
The fairest spot to me,
On the land or on the sea,
Is the charming little cupboard where the
jam-pots grow.

There the sprightly pickles stand,
With the catsup close at hand,
And the marmalades and jellies in a goodly row;
While the quinces' ruddy fire
Would an anchorite inspire
To seek the little cupboard where the jam-pots grow.

Chorus.   Where the jam-pots grow!
Where the jam-pots grow!
Where the jelly jolly, jelly jolly jam-pots
grow.
The fairest spot to me,
On the land or on the sea,
Is the charming little cupboard where the
jam-pots grow.

Never tell me of your bowers
That are full of bugs and flowers!
Never tell me of your meadows where the breezes
blow!
But sing me, if you will,

112

Of the house beneath the hill,
And the darling little cupboard where the jam-pots
grow.

Chorus.   Where the jam-pots grow!
Where the jam-pots grow!
Where the jelly jolly, jelly jolly jam-pots
grow.
The fairest spot to me,
On the land or on the sea,
Is the charming little cupboard where the
jam-pots grow.

THE THREE LITTLE CHICKENS WHO WENT
OUT TO TEA, AND THE ELEPHANT

LITTLE chickens, one, two, three,
They went out to take their tea,
Brisk and gay as gay could be,
   Cackle wackle wackle!
Feathers brushed all smooth and neat,
Yellow stockings on their feet,
Tails and tuftings all complete,
   Cackle wackle wackle!

"Very seldom," said the three,
"Like of us the world can see,
Beautiful exceedingly,
   Cackle wackle wackle!
Such our form and such our face,
Such our Cochin China grace,
We must win in beauty's race,
   Cackle wackle wackle!"

Met an elephant large and wise,
Looked at them with both his eyes:
Caused these chickens great surprise,
   Cackle wackle wackle!
"Why," they said, "do you suppose
Elephant does n't look out of his nose?
So very conveniently it grows!
   Cackle wackle wackle!

"Elephant with nose so long,
Sing us now a lovely song,
As we gayly trip along,
      Cackle wackle wackle!
Sing of us and sing of you,
Sing of corn and barley too,
Beauteous beast with eyes of blue,
      Cackle wackle wackle!"

Elephant sang so loud and sweet,
Chickens fell before his feet;
For his love they did entreat,
      Cackle wackle wackle!
"Well-a-day! and woe is me!
Would we all might elephants be!
Then he'd marry us, one, two, three,
      Cackle wackle wackle!"

Elephant next began to dance :
Capered about with a stately prance
Learned from his grandmother over in France,
      Cackle wackle wackle !
Fast and faster 'gan to tread,
Trod on every chicken's head,
Killed them all uncommonly dead,
      Cackle wackle wackle !

MORAL

Little chickens, one, two, three,
When you 're walking out to tea,
Don't make love to all you see,
      Cackle wackle wackle !
Elephants have lovely eyes,
But to woo them is not wise,
For they are not quite your size !
      Cackle wackle wackle !

MY GRIFFIN

I KEEP my Griffin in the barn;
I keep him busy winding yarn.
I don't let many people see him,
And it would *not* be wise to free him,
For when he opes his jaws so wide,
People might try to look inside,
And then — the things that they would see
Are known to none save only me.

THE UNCLE OF CATO THEOPHILUS JONES

THE uncle of Cato Theophilus Jones,
He sang to his lute in tumultuous tones,
"Oh! twanklety twinklety twanklety twee,
The young Georgiana is lovely to see!"

The young Georgiana (her surname was Grout)
Possessed a Papa who was savage and stout;
He heard from his window the tremulous tones
Of the uncle of Cato Theophilus Jones.

"Now list!" said the parent, "now listen and hark!
Who is it that's warbling thus in the dark?
'Oh! twanklety twinklety twanklety twee,
The young Georgiana is winsome and wee!'"

He seized on a pitcher both ample and full,
And emptied the same on the troubadour's skull,
And the sweet summer evening was filled with the
      groans
Of the uncle of Cato Theophilus Jones.

The maiden may linger and listen full long,
But she never will hear the last words of the song:
"Oh! twanklety twinklety twanklety twee,
The young Georgiana my true love shall be!"

DRINKING VESSELS

BARNABY BLOGGIN
Drank out of a noggin,
And Willoughby Wiggin
Drank out of a piggin.
Gregory Graigh
Made use of a quaigh,
But I am much humbler,
I drink from a tumbler.

AFTER A VISIT TO THE NATURAL
HISTORY MUSEUM

THIS is the Wiggledywasticus,
  Very remarkable beast.
Nose to tail an eighth of a mile;
Took him an acre or two to smile;
Took him a quarter 'f an hour to wink;
Swallowed a pond for his morning drink.
Oh! would it had been vouchsafed to us
Upon the Wiggledywasticus
  Our wondering eyes to feast!

This is the Ptoodlecumtumpsydyl,
  Rather unusual bird.
Had a mouth before and behind;
Ate whichever way he 'd a mind;

Spoiled his digestion, so they say,
Pindled and dwindled quite away,
Or else he might have been living still,
The singular Ptoodlecumtumpsydyl.
    A pity, upon my word!

This is the Ichthyosnortoryx,
    Truly astonishing fish.
Used to snort in a terrible way;
Scared the lobsters to death, they say;
Had a nose like a tea-kettle spout;
Broke it snorting, and so died out.
Sad! if he had n't got into this fix,
We might have made of the 'Snortoryx
    A very acceptable dish.

THE BABY GOES TO BOSTON

WHAT does the train say?
  Jiggle joggle, jiggle joggle!
What does the train say?
  Jiggle joggle jee!
Will the little baby go
Riding with the locomo?
Loky moky poky stoky
Smoky choky chee!

Ting! ting! the bells ring,
  Jiggle joggle, jiggle joggle!
Ting! ting! the bells ring,
  Jiggle joggle jee!
Ring for joy because we go
Riding with the locomo,
Loky moky poky stoky
  Smoky choky chee!

Look! how the trees run,
  Jiggle joggle, jiggle joggle!
Each chasing t' other one,
  Jiggle joggle jee!
Are they running for to go
Riding with the locomo?
Loky moky poky stoky
  Smoky choky chee!

Over the hills now,
  Jiggle joggle, jiggle joggle!

Down through the vale below,
　Jiggle joggle jee!
All the cows and horses run,
Crying, "Won't you take us on,
Loky moky poky stoky
　Smoky choky chee?"

So, so, the miles go,
　Jiggle joggle, jiggle joggle!
Now it's fast and now it's slow,
　Jiggle joggle jee!
When we're at our journey's end,
Say good-by to snorting friend,
Loky moky poky stoky
　Smoky choky chee!

THE LITTLE GNOME

ONCE there lived a little gnome
Who had made his little home
Right down in the middle of the earth, earth, earth.
He was full of fun and frolic,
But his wife was melancholic,
And he never could divert her into mirth, mirth, mirth.

He had tried her with a monkey
And a parrot and a donkey,
And a pig that squealed whene'er he pulled its tail, tail,
tail.
But though he laughed himself
Into fits, the jolly elf,
Still his wifey's melancholy did not fail, fail, fail.

"I will hie me," said the gnome,
"From my worthy earthy home;
I will go among the dwellings of the men, men, men.
Something funny there must be,
That will make her say, 'He, he!'
I will find it and will bring it her again, 'gain, 'gain."

So he travelled here and there,
And he saw the Blinking Bear,
And the Pattypol whose eyes are in his tail, tail, tail.
And he saw the Linking Gloon,
Who was playing the bassoon,
And the Octopus a-waltzing with the whale, whale,
whale.

He saw the Chingo Chee,
And a lovely sight was he,
With a ringlet and a ribbon on his nose, nose, nose,
And the Baggle, and the Wogg,
And the Cantilunar Dog,
Who was throwing cotton-flannel at his foes, foes, foes.

All these the little gnome
Transported to his home,
And set them down before his weeping wife, wife, wife;
But she only cried and cried,
And she sobbywobbed and sighed,
Till she really was in danger of her life, life, life.

Then the gnome was in despair,
And he tore his purple hair,
And he sat him down in sorrow on a stone, stone, stone.
"I, too," he said, "will cry,
Till I tumble down and die,
For I 've had enough of laughing all alone, 'lone, 'lone."

His tears they flowed away,
Like a rivulet at play,
With a bubble, gubble, rubble, o'er the ground, ground, ground.
But when this his wifey saw,
She loudly cried "Haw, haw!
Here at last is something funny you have found, found, found."

She laughed, "Ho, ho! he, he!"
And she chuckled loud with glee,
And she wiped away her little husband's tears, tears,
   tears.
   And since then, through wind and weather,
   They have said, "He, he!" together,
For several hundred thousand merry years, years, years.

BINGO THE DINGO AND THE FATAL
FLAMINGO

THE Dingo, the Dingo,
He went by the name of Bingo.
   He went very well
   Until he fell
In love with the fatal Flamingo.

Flamingo, Flamingo,
The fatally fair flamingo,
   No mate was she,
   As you 'll readily see,
For quadrupedantical Dingo.

"Flamingo, Flamingo,
Oh say, will you wed with Bingo?
   My coat is but yellow,
   But still I 'm a fellow
Whose friends think him rather a Stingo."

A Stingo, a Stingo,
So that 's what they thought of Bingo;
   (He was nought of the sort,
   He was merely — in short,
He was nothing at all but a Dingo.)

Flamingo, Flamingo,
She scornfully stared at Bingo;
   And said, "Go away!
   I cannot to-day
Take the trouble to follow your lingo!"

His lingo! his lingo!
A cruel remark for Bingo,
 He knew how to bark
 In the dawn and the dark,
And he almost had learned how to sing, oh!

Flamingo, Flamingo,
Paid no more attention to Bingo.
 She stood with a smile,
 On the bank of the Nile,
And thought, "By and by I will in go!"

The Dingo, the Dingo,
Repulsed by the cruel Flamingo,
  Rushed into the wave
  To his watery grave,
And that was the end of poor Bingo.

THE GINGHAM UMBRELLA

[A Lesson in Politeness]

ALPHONSO, Alphonso, Alphonso and Arabella,
  They happened to meet
  A man in the street,
Who carried a gingham umbrella.

Alphonso possessed neither manners nor grace,
He made at this person a hideous face;
But how different the conduct of sweet Arabella,
Who praised with politeness the gingham umbrella.

The man was a nobleman, deeply disguised;
The compliment courteous he pointedly prized;
"Sweet creature," he said, "come away from this
    feller,
And take both my heart and my gingham umbrella!"

The very next morning they met in the church,
And foolish Alphonso was left in the lurch;
For they said, "In the future you 'll know how to tell a
Great lord from a loon, by his gingham umbrella!"

131

THE ADVENTUROUS GRASSHOPPER

THERE was a Grasshopper lived in a palm tree,
 Silver-voiced as a frog in June ;
Was not pleased with his situation,
 Thought he 'd like to go to the moon.
  Oh ! hi ho !
  How shall I get there, oh ?
  A hop and a skip, a flop and a flip,
  And up through the clouds I 'll go.

Off he went like a streak of lightning,
 Lit on the moon like a thunderbolt ;
Naught could he see but a man with a lantern,
 Riding about on a pea-green colt.
  Oh ! hi ho !
  Why did I come here, oh ?
  A fling and a swing, a flap of my wing,
  And back to the earth I 'll go.

Off he shot like a blazing rocket,
 Down he came like a falling star ;
What should he meet but a gay little goshawk,
 Flying up from the earth so far.
  Oh ! hi ho !
  Poor little Grasshopper, oh !
  A snap and a squeak in the bonny bird's beak,
  There was an end of him, oh !

THE LITTLE DUTCHESS

ONCE there lived a little Dutchess,
Just beside the Zuyder Zee;
Short and stout and roly-poly,
As a Dutchess ought to be.

She had pigs and she had poultry,
She had lands and she had gold;
And she loved the Burgomaster, —
Loved him more than can be told.

"Surly, burly Burgomaster,
Will you have me for your love?
You shall be my pouter-pigeon,
I will be your turtle-dove.

"You shall have my China porkers,
You shall have each Dorking hen;
Take them with your loving Dutchess,
Oh, you Dutchiest of men!"

Loudly laughed the Burgomaster,
"Naught I care for Dorking fowls;
Naught for pig, unless 't is roasted,
And on that my doctor scowls.

"Frumpy, stumpy little Dutchess,
I do not incline to wed.
Keep your pigs and keep your poultry!
I will take your gold instead.

"I will take your shining florins,
I will take your fields' rich hoard;
You may go and tend your piggies
Till your spirits be restored."

Loudly wept the little Dutchess,
Tending sad each China pig;
Loudly laughed the Burgomaster
'Neath his merry periwig.

Till the Dutchy people, angry
Conduct such as this to see,
Took and plumped the pouter-pigeon
Right into the Zuyder Zee.

BOBBILY BOO AND WOLLYPOTUMP

BOBBILY Boo, the king so free,
He used to drink the Mango tea.
Mango tea and coffee, too,
He drank them both till his nose turned blue.

Wollypotump, the queen so high,
She used to eat the Gumbo pie.
Gumbo pie and Gumbo cake,
She ate them both till her teeth did break.

Bobbily Boo and Wollypotump,
Each called the other a greedy frump.
And when these terrible words were said,
They sat and cried till they both were dead.

IN FOREIGN PARTS

WHEN I lived in Singapore,
It was something of a bore
To receive the bulky Begums who came trundling to
    my door ;
They kept getting into tangles
With their bingle-bongle-bangles,
And the tiger used to bite them as he sat upon the
    floor.

When I lived in Timbuctoo,
Almost every one I knew
Used to play upon the sackbut, singing "toodle-doodle-
    doo",
And they made ecstatic ballads,
And consumed seductive salads,
Made of chicory and hickory and others things that
    grew.

When I lived in Rotterdam,
I possessed a spotted ram,
Who would never feed on anything but hollyhocks and
      ham;
But one day he butted down
All the magnates of the town,
So they slew him, though I knew him to be gentle as a
      lamb.

                    But!

When I got to Kandahar,
It was very, very far,
And the people came and said to me, "How *very* plain
      you are!"
So I sailed across the foam,
And I toddle-waddled home,
And no more I 'll go a-rovering beyond the harbor bar.

FUSSY

THERE was a little funny man
Lived down our street;
Pettitoes and pottytoes
Were all that he would eat.

When they were out of season,
He never asked the reason,
But banging on the butcher's door,
Arrested him for treason.

THE OUTLANDISHMAN

The Outlandishman came o'er the sea, o'er the sea,
  In a skipaway flipaway boat;
And who so merry, so merry as he,
  As soon as he got afloat?

He sat on the poop to gobble his soup
  With a spoon, with a spoon of the best;
And part of his fast he broke on the mast,
  And smashed on the bowsprit the rest.

He lowered his line in the deep, in the deep,
  And invited the fishlikins up;
Then he hung them in rows in front of his nose,
  And wished it were time to sup.

Then the Bottlegreen Bovis arose, arose,
  And asked was he game for a fight;
But he seized on the anchor and threw it with rancor,
  And the foe-fish retired from sight.

He danced on the deck with never a check
  Till the clock, till the clock struck nine.
And his eyes did wink, and he sang "tink a tink!"
  In the mowl of the merry moonshine.

Lo! all of these things the Outlandishman did,
  As he sailed, as he sailed on the sea.
Yea, more! yea, more! both sorry and sore,
  But you never shall learn them from me.

A SPANISH BALLAD

A GENTLEMAN in fair Madrid
He loved a lovely maid, he did;
Of all the maids the pearl and pink,
Oh, tink-a-tink-a-tink-a-tink!

He followed her both near and far,
Performing on his light guitar;
And often at her feet he sank,
Oh, tank-a-tank-a-tank-a-tank!

But she remained both grim and grave ;
"I wish," she said, "you would behave !"
And so he went and was a monk,
Oh, tunk-a-tunk-a-tunk-a-tunk !

THE STRANGE BEAST

FOUR gay gallants of London town
Went out to walk on Horsley Down;
   And there they saw a beast,
The like of which had ne'er been seen
In Cheapside or in Strand, I ween,
   In West-side or in East.

Its legs were four, its tail was one,
So one gallant swore by the sun
   It therefore was a horse.
"Nay!" cried the next, "this talk is idle.
If 't were a horse, 't would have a bridle,
   A saddle, too, of course."

"It has a horn, you will perceive,
We 'll therefore call it, by your leave,
   A unicorn of pride."
The others vowed by stick and fiddle
The unicorn wore his horn in the middle,
   And not upon the side.

"I call 't a lion!" said the third.
"Nay!" cried the fourth, "that's *too* absurd!
   The creature has no mane.
To one who has a judgment fair,
It would appear to be a bear;
   And this I will maintain."

The beast (I 'll tell the secret now!
'T was Farmer Giles's one-horned cow;
    Her other horn was broken)
Advanced, meanwhile, toward the four,
And as 't was supper-time and more,
    Mooed loud, by way of token.

With shriek and scream those gallants gay
To London town fled back away,
    As fast as they might fare.
And when at home they stopped to rest 'em,
A whole menagerie had chased 'em,
    As every one could swear.

WAS SHE A WITCH?

THERE was an old woman
    Lived down in a dell;
She used to draw picklejacks
    Out of the well.
How did she do it?
Nobody knew it,
    She never, no never, no never would tell.

THE GARGOYLE AND THE GRIFFIN

ONCE a Gargoyle and a Griffin
Thought they 'd go and take their tiffin
With the eminent Confucius, just outside the temple
wall ;
So they started off together,
In the charming Chinese weather,
But when they reached the spot, Confucius was n't
there at all.

He had gone to the Bazaar, sir,
With his little cup and sarcer,
For an emptiness was in him that he could not well
abide ;
And there he saw a Gorgon,
Who was playing on the organ,
A sight that 's rare in China, and in other lands be-
side.

The Gargoyle and the Griffin
Gave a mournful, scornful sniff in
The direction of the temple, then they followed on his
track ;
For they said, "There may be food there,
And the cigarettes are good there,
And if Confushy does not treat, we 'll treat him — to
a whack !"

So they toddled on together
In the charming Chinese weather,

Till they reached the great Bazaar where all the people
   used to go.
And they too saw the Gorgon,
Who was playing on the organ,
And they said, "What may this creature be, we do
   not, do not know!"

Now Confucius was retiring
In his nature, and admiring,
He stood behind the Gorgon while he listened to her
   lay;
But the other two stood staring
With their goggle-eyes a-glaring,
Till the Gorgon chanced to look at them; and then —
   alas, the day!

Said the Gargoyle to the Griffin,
"Sir, I feel a trifle stiff in
My joints, and I propose that we retire from this spot!"
Said the Griffin to the other,
"I would gladly go, my brother,
But a feeling's o'er me stealing that retire I — can —
   not!"

Not for long they made their moan there;
They were both turned into stone there,
And their stony, bony carcasses adorned the public way;
While the cheerful little Gorgon
Played away upon her organ,
And enjoyed herself immensely the remainder of the
   day.

But the Eminent Confucius
Cried aloud, "My goodness *grucious!*
My neighbors are converted into granite in my sight.
Let me flee from this Bazaar, sir,
With my little cup and sarcer,
For really, for the moment, I have lost my appetite!"

JOHNNY'S BY-LOW SONG

HERE on our rock-away horse we go,
Johnny and I, to a land we know, —
Far away in the sunset gold,
A lovelier land than can be told.

Chorus.   Where all the flowers go niddlety nod,
Nod, nod, niddlety nod!
Where all the flowers go niddlety nod,
And all the birds sing by-low!
Lullaby, lullaby, by-low.

The gates are ivory set with pearls,
One for the boys, and one for the girls:
So shut your bonny two eyes of blue,
Or else they never will let you through.

Chorus.   Where all the flowers go niddlety nod,
Nod, nod, niddlety nod!
Where all the flowers go niddlety nod,
And all the birds sing by-low!
Lullaby, lullaby, by-low.

But what are the children all about?
There 's never a laugh and never a shout.
Why, they all fell asleep, dear, long ago;
For how could they keep awake, you know?

Chorus.   When all the flowers went niddlety nod,
Nod, nod, niddlety nod!
When all the flowers went niddlety nod,

149

And all the birds sang by-low!
Lullaby, lullaby, by-low.

And each little brown or golden head
Is pillowed soft in a satin bed, —
A satin bed with sheets of silk,
As soft as down and as white as milk.

Chorus.   And all the flowers go niddlety nod,
　　　　　Nod, nod, niddlety nod!
　　　　　And all the flowers go niddlety nod,
　　　　　And all the birds sing by-low!
　　　　　Lullaby, lullaby, by-low.

The brook in its sleep goes babbling by,
And the fat little clouds are asleep in the sky:
And now little Johnny is sleeping too,
So open the gates and pass him through.

Chorus.   Where all the flowers go niddlety nod,
　　　　　Nod, nod, niddlety nod!
　　　　　Where all the flowers go niddlety nod,
　　　　　And all the birds sing by-low!
　　　　　Lullaby, lullaby, by-low.

GEOGRAPHI

[AIR : *There was a maid in my countree.*]

THERE was a man in Manitobá,
The only man that ever was thar ;
His name was Nicholas Jones McGee,
And he loved a maid in Mirimichi.

Chorus. Sing ha ! ha ! ha ! for Manitobá !
Sing he ! he ! he ! for Mirimichi !
Sing hi ! hi ! hi ! for Geographi !
And that 's the lesson for you and me.

There was a man in New Mexico,
He lost his grandmother out in the snow ;
But his heart was light, and his ways were free,
So he bought him another in Santa Fé.

Chorus. Sing ho ! ho ! ho ! for New Mexico !
Sing he ! he ! he ! for Santa Fé !

Sing hi! hi! hi! for Geographi!
And that's the lesson for you and me.

There was a man in Aus-tra-li-*a*,
He sat and wept on the new-mown hay:
He jumped on the tail of a kangaroo,
And rode till he came to Kalamazoo.

Chorus. Sing hey! hey! hey! for Aus-tra-li-*a*!
Sing hoo! hoo! hoo! for Kalamazoo!
Sing hi! hi! hi! for Geographi!
And that's the lesson for me and you.

There was a man in Jiggerajum,
He went to sea in a kettle-drum;
He sailed away to the Salisbury Shore,
And I never set eyes on that man any more.

Chorus. Sing hum! hum! hum! for Jiggerajum!
Sing haw! haw! haw! for the Salisbury Shore!
Sing hi! hi! hi! for Geographi!
And that's the lesson the whole world o'er

HIGGLEDY-PIGGLEDY

HIGGLEDY-PIGGLEDY went to school,
Looking so nice and neat!
Clean little mittens on clean little hands,
Clean little shoes on his feet.
Jacket and trousers all nicely brushed,
Collar and cuffs like snow.
"See that you come home as neat to-night,
Higgledy-piggledy oh!"

Higgledy-piggledy came from school,
In such a woful plight,
All the people he met on the road
Ran screaming away with fright.
One shoe gone for ever and aye,
T' other one stiff with mud,
Dirt-spattered jacket half torn from his back,
Mittens both lost in the wood.

Higgledy-piggledy stayed in bed
All a long, pleasant day,
While his father fished for his other boot
In the roadside mud and clay.
All day long his mother must mend.
Wash and iron and sew,
Before she can make him fit to be seen,
Higgledy-piggledy oh!

BELINDA BLONDE

BELINDA BLONDE was a beautiful doll,
With rosy-red cheeks and a flaxen poll.
Her lips were red, and her eyes were blue,
But to say she was happy would not be true;
For she pined for love of the great big Jack
Who lived in the Box so grim and black.

She never had looked on the Jack his face;
But she fancied it shining with beauty and grace,
And all the day long she would murmur and pout,
Because Jack-in-the-box would never come out.

"Oh, beautiful, beautiful Jack-in-the-box,
Undo your bolts and undo your locks!
The cupboard is shut, and there's no one about:
Oh! Jack-in-the-box, jump out! jump out!"

But alas! alas! for Belinda Blonde,
And alas! alas! for her dreamings fond.
There soon was an end to all her doubt,
For Jack-in-the-box really *did* jump out! —

Out with a crash and out with a spring,
Half black and half scarlet, a horrible thing.
Out with a yell and a shriek and a shout,
His great goggle-eyes glaring wildly about.

"And what did Belinda do?" you say.
Alas! before she could get out of the way,
The monster struck her full on the head,
And with pain and with terror she fell down dead.

MORAL

Now all you dolls, both little and big,
With china crown and with curling wig,
Before you give way to affection fond,
Remember the fate of Belinda Blonde!
And unless you 're fond of terrible knocks,
Don't set your heart on a Jack-in-the-box!

STORY-TELL

"TELL me about a funny old man!"
"And so I will! his name was Dan.
He lived in the town of Wumpston Wells,
In a house made out of oyster shells.
The oysters hung about inside,
And when he wanted some, broiled or fried,
He held his pipkin up a minute,
And down they fell, all ready in it.
The chairs were made of peanut brittle,
Yes, every one, both big and little;
The cushions all of plummy cake;
And — " "Did it make his tummy ache?"
"It did, my dear! the wisest plan
Will be to say no more of Dan."

"About a funny old woman, then!"
"Well! *she* — her name was Hepzibah N.
What is N. for? For Ninnycumtwitch,

Or Niddlecumdinky, I don't know which —
The funny thing about her was
She never could hold her tongue, because
'T was hung in the middle, and wagged at both ends,
A serious trial to all her friends;
For when they wanted to ask her to dinner,
They had to *gag* her, as I 'm a sinner.
Then she would go home in a terrible huff,
And say she had n't had half enough;
And they would say, 'Oh!' — and then — and then —
I think that 's enough about Hepzibah N."

"Then tell — oh, tell about an ogre!"
"Well! there was one who wore a toga.
He said, 'It is the proper fashion!'
He went into a frightful passion
Because his uncles and the rest
Still clung to trousers, coat and vest.
He gnashed his teeth; he
    screamed and roared,
Until his uncles all were
    bored.
They wopsed him up
    within his toga,
And sent him off to Sara-
    toga.
I 've heard no further
    word about him,
But we do very well with-
    out him."

JACKY FROST

Jacky Frost, Jacky Frost,
   Came in the night;
Left the meadows that he crossed
   All gleaming white.
Painted with his silver brush
   Every window-pane;
Kissed the leaves and made them blush,
   Blush and blush again.

Jacky Frost, Jacky Frost,
   Crept around the house,
Sly as a silver fox,
   Still as a mouse.
Out little Jenny came,
   Blushing like a rose;
Up jumped Jacky Frost,
   And pinched her little nose.

THE BALLAD OF THE BEACH

"Take off thy stockings, Samuel!
  Now take them off, I pray;
Roll up thy trousers, Samuel,
  And come with me to play.

"The ebbing tide has left the sand
  All hard and smooth and white,
And we will build a goodly fort,
  And have a goodly fight."

Then Samuel he pullèd off
  His hose of scarlet hue,
And Samuel he rollèd up
  His breeches darkly blue.

And hand-in-hand with Reginald,
  He hied him to the beach;
Each little boy a shovel had,
  And eke a pail had each.

Then down upon the shining sand
  Right joyfully they sat;
And far upon the shining sand
  Each tossed his broad-brimmed hat.

Then valiantly to work they went,
  Like sturdy lads and true;
And there they built a stately fort,
  The best that they might do.

"Now sit we down within the walls,
    Which rise above our head,
And we will make us cannon-balls
    Of sand, as good as lead."

Now as they worked, these little boys,
    Full glad in heart and mind,
The creeping tide came back again,
    To see what it could find.

The creeping tide came up the sand,
    To see what it could do;
And there it found two broad-brimmed hats,
    With ribbons red and blue.

And "See now!" said the creeping tide;
    "These hats belong, I trow,
To Reginald and Samuel;
    I saw them here but now."

And "See now!" said the creeping tide;
    "What hinders me to float
These hats out to the boys' mamma,
    Is sailing in a boat?"

Then up there came two little waves,
    All rippling so free;
They lifted up the broad-brimmed hats,
    And bore them out to sea.

The ribbons red and ribbons blue
    Streamed gallantly away;

The straw did glitter in the sun,
    Was never craft so gay!

The mother of these little lads
    Was sailing on the sea;
And now she laughed, and now she sang,
    And who so blithe as she?

And "Look!" she said; "what things be these
    That dance upon the wave,
All fluttering and glittering
    And sparkling so brave?

"Now row me well, my brethren twain,
    Now row me o'er the sea!
For we will chase these tiny craft,
    And see what they may be."

They rowed her fast, they rowed her well, —
    Too well, those gallants true;
For when she reached the broad-brimmed hats,
    Right well those hats she knew.

"Alas!" she cried; "my little lads
    Are drownèd in the sea!"
Then down she sank in deadly swoon,
    As pale as she might be.

They rowed her well, those gallants gay,
    They rowed her to the land;
They lifted up that lady pale,
    And bore her up the strand.

But as they bore her up the beach,
    The balls began to fly,
And hit those gallants on the nose,
    And hit them in the eye.

They lookèd here, they lookèd there,
    To see whence this might be;
And soon they spied a stately fort,
    Beside the salt, salt sea.

And straight from out the stately fort
    The balls were flying free;
Each gallant rubbed his smitten nose,
    And eke his eye rubbed he.

They looked within the stately fort,
    To see who aimed so well;
And there was little Reginald,
    And youthful Samuel.

They lifted up those little lads,
    Each by his waisty-band;
And down beside that lady pale
    They set them on the sand.

And first that lady waxed more pale,
    And syne she waxed full red;
And syne she kissed those little boys,
    But not a word she said.

Then up and spoke those gallants gay,
    "You naughty little chaps,

Your poor mamma you 've frightened sore,
  And made her ill, perhaps.

"And if you are not shaken well,
  And if you are not spanked,
It will not be your uncles' fault ;
  So *they* need not be thanked."

Then up and spoke those little lads,
  All mournful as they sat ;
And each did cry, "Ah, woe is me !
  I 've lost — my nice — new — hat !"

Then up and spoke that lady fair,
  "Nay, nay, my little dears,
You sha' n't be spanked ! so come with me,
  And wipe away your tears.

"There be more hats in Boston town,
  For little boys to wear ;
And as for those that you have lost,
  I pray their voyage be fair.

"For since I have my little lads,
  The hats may sail away
Around the world and back again,
  Forever and a day !"

GREGORY GRIGGS

Gregory Griggs, Gregory Griggs,
Had forty-seven different wigs;
He wore them up, and he wore them down,
To please the people of Boston town.
He wore them east, and he wore them west,
But he never could tell which he liked the best.

A NURSERY TRAGEDY

IT was a lordly elephant,
His name, his name was Sprite;
He stood upon the nursery floor,
All ready for a fight.

He looked upon the rocking-horse,
Who proudly prancing stood:
"O rocking-horse! O shocking horse!
I 'm thirsting for your blood!

"How dare you stand and look at me,
You ugly snorting thing?
Know, that of every living beast,
The elephant is king!

"And if a person looks at me,
Unless I give him leave,
He 's very apt to meet his death
Too swiftly for reprieve.

"You are the most unpleasant beast
I e'er have looked on yet;
Although the stupid children here
Will make of you a pet.

"I hate your tail of waving hair!
I hate your bits of brass!
But more, oh, more than all, I hate
Your gleaming eyes of glass!

"Were you of cotton-flannel made,
As nursery beasts should be,
With eyes of good black boot-buttons,
You then might look at me.

"I might forgive your want of tusks,
Your lack of trunk forgive;
But that wild, goggling, glassy glare —
No! never, while I live!

"So get you gone, you rocking-horse!
Go to your closet-shed,
And there, behind the wood-basket,
Conceal your ugly head!"

But as the elephant thus did scold
And rage and fume and roar,
The rocking-horse rocked over him,
And crushed him to the floor.

SPOTS AND STRIPES

A LIVELY young leopard,
With spots gaily peppered,
He met with an ocelot,
Gallant and gay.
Said one to the other,
"Your spots are wrong, brother!
The kind I am wearing 's
The fashion to-day!"

"You really can*not*, sir,
Wear that kind of spot, sir!"
The ocelot cried,
With a curl of his nose.
"You 'd best be arranging
For speedily changing;
You 'd *like* to be stylish,
I rather suppose?"

"Silly ass!" cried the leopard,
"Believe me, you jeopard *
Your safety in using
Such language as this.
The leopard does not, sir,
Make change in his spot, sir;
The world knows the proverb,
I wot and I wis."

* He was proud of this word; he thought it scholastic, but i\
is not in the dictionary.

168

"Fizz!" hissed the one proudly,
"Miaow!" t' other cried loudly,
And each for the other
Ferociously went,
With impetus savage
To ramp and to ravage,
With lashings and bashings
Of dreadful intent.

BUT OH!
SEE WHAT HAPPENED!

Every great Cat in the jungle, jungle,
Every great Cat that could be,
Hearing the noise, as if he 'd been stungle,
Came loping along the lea.

The Puma
Heard the rumor;
The Ounce
Made a pounce;
The Lynx
Brought his winks;
The Panther
(Named Samantha!)
The Cheetah
(No one fleeter)
The Jaguar —
"What a wag you are!"
He said unto the Bob Cat
Who seemed to be a snob cat.

And they all
'Gan to squall
In a fell and feline brawl,
"Our spots are finer far than any other!"
And they clawed and hissed and spat,
Every spotted, dotted cat,
Till you could n't tell 'em one from another.

But a lordly Tiger, strolling
   From the jungle of Bengal,
Saw them where they lay a-rolling,
   Heard them screech and heard them squall.
"Cease your strife, you dowdy Creatures!
Stripes are what Dame Fashion features,
Spots, I hear, are n't 'in' at all!"

WIGGLE AND WAGGLE AND BUBBLE AND SQUEAK

Wiggle and Waggle and Bubble and Squeak,
They went their fortunes for to seek;
They went to sea in a chicken-coop,
And they lived on mulligatawney soup.

Wiggle and Waggle and Bubble and Squeak,
They cooked their soup every day in the week;
They cooked their soup in a chimney-pot,
For there the water was always hot.

Wiggle and Waggle and Bubble and Squeak,
Each gave the other one's nose a tweak;
They tweaked so hard that it took their breath,
And so they met an untimely death.

GOOD ADVICE

IF you are a Janissary,
Go and catch a cassowary,
    (If the bird you lack!)
Bridle him and saddle him,
Quickly then bestraddle him;
    Go, and *don't come back!*

N.B.   If, as is quite possible, you are *not* a Janissary, do something entirely different.   There are plenty of things!

If you are a Functionary,
Don't be brusque and bunctionary;
    Be benign and bland!
When you meet a cross curmudgeon,
Don't bethump him with a bludgeon;
    Spank him with your hand!

N.B.   Functionaries are of various kinds;   the bunctionary
ones are never popular; in this case I mean a policeman, but he
has not syllables enough.

THE THIRSTY BIRDS

THE penguin and the pelican,
  The spoonbill and the stork,
They wanted a drink,
But what do you think?
  They could n't pull out the cork!

The ginger beer was bright and clear,
  It sparkled in the bottle.
But there it was shut
As close as a nut,
  And never a drop for their throttle.

A portly hippopotamus
  Came rolling down the lane;
And "Oh!" they cried,
"Now well betide!
  He 'll ease us of our pain."

They told their tale with weep and wail;
  The 'potamus he listened;

174

And all the while
With greed and guile
   His little eyes they glistened.

"O penguin and O pelican,
   O spoonbill and O stork,
Hand over here
Your ginger beer,
   I 'll see about the cork!"

He took the bottle 'tween his teeth,
   And swallowed of it whole!
Then with a wink,
"A pleasant drink!"
   He said, and off did roll.

The thirsty birds looked after him,
   And oh, but they were sad!
But when he had a tummy ache
That made his portly frame to quake,
And *almost* into pieces break,
   They all were *VERY GLAD!*

OLD JOE JONES

OLD Joe Jones and his old dog Bones,
Go jigglety-joggle over the stones;
He sells meat-pies and fishery-fries;
"Heat 'em and eat 'em!" all day he cries.
If we don't buy them, he moans and groans,
Old Joe Jones and his old dog Bones.

A BRIEF BALLAD OF ARABY

In Araby, in Araby,
In Araby the blest,
There lived a man who thought he 'd like
To travel to the west.
On a lumpy humpy camel he
Departed with his family;
His uncle's name was Sammy Lee,
But I forget the rest.

From Araby, from Araby,
From Araby the free,
They amble-ramble-gambolled
Till they came unto the sea.
But the camel could not swim, you know,
It disagreed with him, you know,
He waved his hinder limb, you know,
And yelled ferociously.

To Araby, to Araby,
To Araby the fair,
They turned their faces home again
In anguish and despair.
But the camel, they 'd such grief of him,
They wished to find relief of him,
And so they made corned beef of him,
And ate him then and there.

FROM NEW YORK TO BOSTON

[Allegro con moto]

HERE we go skilfully skipping,
Riding the resonant rail;
Conductor the tickets is clipping,
Boy has bananas for sale.
Raindrops outside are a-dripping, —
Dripping o'er meadow and vale.
Here we go skilfully skipping,
Riding the resonant rail.

Clankety clankety clank,
Clinkety clinkety cling;
Five little boys on a bank,
One little girl in a swing.
Fishhawk o'erhead in the distance,
Spreading his wings like a sail.
Here we go skilfully skipping,
Riding the resonant rail.

"Puck, Life, Frank Leslie, and Harper!
Latest editions, just out!"
Boy is an impudent sharper!
All are last week's, I 've no doubt.
"Every new monthly and weekly,
Every new novel and tale!"
Here we go skilfully skipping,
Riding the resonant rail.

Jogglety jogglety joggle!
Jigglety jigglety jig!
Snuffy old man with a goggle,
Acid old dame with a wig,
Pretty girl peacefully sleeping
Under her gold-spotted veil.
Here we go skilfully skipping,
Riding the resonant rail.

Now we are duly admonished,
Hartford 's the place we reach next;
Cow in the field looks astonished,
Sheep in the pasture perplexed.
Furious puppy pursues us,
Cocking a truculent tail.
Here we go skilfully skipping,
Riding the resonant rail.

"Lozenges, peanuts, and candy!
Apples and oranges sweet!"
Legs are so frightfully bandy,
Wonder he keeps on his feet.
"All the New York evening papers, —
Times, Tribune, World, Sun, and Mail!"
Here we go skilfully skipping,
Riding the resonant rail.

Engine goes "Whoosh!" at the station,
Engine goes "Whizz!" o'er the plain;
Horses express consternation,
Drivers remonstrate in vain.

Smoke-witches dancing about us,
Sparks in a fiery train.
Here we go skilfully skipping,
Riding the resonant rail.

Tinklety tinklety tink!
Tunklety tunklety tunk!
Nearing the station, I think.
Where is the check for my trunk?
"Boston!" and "Boston!" and "Boston!"
Home of my fathers, all hail!
Here we go joyfully jumping,
Away from the resonant rail.

PUMP AND PLANET

WITH a hop, skip, and jump,
We went to the pump,
To fill our kettles with starch.
He gave us good day
In the pleasantest way,
With a smile that was winning and arch.

"Oh, Pump," said I,
"When you look up on high
To flirt with the morning star,
Does it make you sad,
Oh! Pumpy, my lad,
To think she 's away so far?"

Said the Pump, "Oh no!
For we 've settled it so
That but little my feelings are tried.
For every clear night
She slides down the moonlight,
And shines in the trough at my side."

THE DIFFERENCE

EIGHT fingers,
Ten toes,
Two eyes,
And one nose.
Baby said
When she smelt the rose,
"Oh! what a pity
I 've only one nose!"

Ten teeth
In even rows,
Three dimples,
And one nose.
Baby said
When she smelt the snuff,
"Deary me!
One nose is enough."

THE HORNET AND THE BEE

SAID the hornet to the bee,
"Pray you, will you marry me?
Will you be my little wife,
For to love me all my life?
You shall have a velvet cloak,
And a bonnet with a poke.
You shall sit upon a chair
With a cabbage in your hair.
You shall ride upon a horse,
If you fancy such a course.
You shall feed on venison pasty
In a manner trig and tasty;
Devilled bones and apple-cores,
If you like them, shall be yours.
You shall drink both rum and wine,
If you only will be mine.
Pray you, will you marry me?"
Said the hornet to the bee.

Said the bee unto the hornet,
"Your proposal, sir, I scorn it.
Marry one devoid of money,
Who can't make a drop of honey?
Cannot even play the fiddle,
And is pinched up in the middle?
Nay, my love is set more high;
Cockychafer's bride am I.
Cockychafer whirring loud,
Frisking free and prancing proud,

Cockychafer blithe and gay,
He hath stole my heart away.
Him alone I mean to marry,
So no longer you need tarry.
Not another moment stay !
Cockychafer comes this way.
Your proposal, sir, I scorn it !"
Said the bee unto the hornet.

So the cockychafer came,
Took the bee to be his dame.
Took the bee to be his wife,
For to love her all his life.
Wedding dress of goblin green,
Hat and feathers for a queen,
Worsted mittens on her feet,
Thus her toilet was complete.
Then when it was time to dine,
Cockychafer brought her wine,
Roasted mouse and bunny-fish,
Porridge in a silver dish ;
Lobster-claws and scalloped beast.
Was not that a lovely feast ?
But when it was time to sup,
Cockychafer ate her up.
Thus concludes the history
Of the hornet and the bee.

PUNKYDOODLE AND JOLLAPIN

Oh, Pillykin Willykin Winky Wee!
How does the Emperor take his tea?
He takes it with melons, he takes it with milk,
He takes it with syrup and sassafras silk.
He takes it without, he takes it within.
Oh, Punkydoodle and Jollapin!

Oh, Pillykin Willykin Winky Wee!
How does the Cardinal take his tea?
He takes it in Latin, he takes it in Greek,

He takes it just seventy times in the week.
He takes it so strong that it makes him grin.
Oh, Punkydoodle and Jollapin!

Oh, Pillykin Willykin Winky Wee!
How does the Admiral take his tea?
He takes it with splices, he takes it with spars,
He takes it with jokers and jolly jack tars.
And he stirs it round with a dolphin's fin.
Oh, Punkydoodle and Jollapin!

Oh, Pillykin Willykin Winky Wee!
How does the President take his tea?
He takes it in bed, he takes it in school,
He takes it in Congress against the rule.
He takes it with brandy, and thinks it no sin.
Oh, Punkydoodle and Jollapin!

THE OWL AND THE EEL AND THE
WARMING-PAN

THE owl and the eel and the warming-pan,
They went to call on the soap-fat man.
The soap-fat man he was not within:
He 'd gone for a ride on his rolling-pin.
So they all came back by the way of the town,
And turned the meeting-house upside down.

KINDNESS TO ANIMALS

Riddle cum diddle cum dido,
My little dog's name is Fido;
  I bought him a wagon,
  And hitched up a dragon,
And off we both went for a ride, oh!

Riddle cum diddle cum doodle,
My little cat's name is Toodle;
  I curled up her hair,
  But she only said, "There!
You have made me look *just* like a poodle!"

Riddle cum diddle cum dinky,
My little pig's name is Winkie;
  I keep him quite clean
  With the washing machine,
And I rinse him all off in the sinkie.

INDEX OF FIRST LINES